BRAD AND ADAM SERIES

What's your Financial Game Plan?

The Workbook

Neala Okuromade

First published in Great Britain in 2017 by Brad & Adam Publishing Ltd

www.whatsyourfinancialgameplan.com

ISBN: 978-0-9575045-2-3

Cover: Emmantech Creative Solutions, www.emmantech.com

Editor and Typesetter: Claire Handy of Handy Editorials, www.handyeditorials.co.uk

Table of Contents

About the Author

Neala Okuromade is known for her passion aimed at personal finance. She is the author of the book *What's Your Financial Gameplan?* which deals with personal finance issues, founded on a long fascination for implementing practical solutions to everyday money problems.

With over fourteen years' experience in accounting, Neala is a member of the 'Association of Certified Chartered Accountants' during which time she has managed finance departments. Her experience includes: Project Accountant for a large Property Company, where she supervised a multimillion-pound project setting up the finance systems and procedures; a Financial Controller of a Property Exchange Service Company, which was later bought out by an American Nasdaq listed company; and the Associate Director of Finance for one of the most reputable charities in England and Wales at the time.

Neala is passionate about empowering the everyday person to make a success of their personal finances, especially in today's tough and chaotic economic climate. An avid studier of world financial news, economics and investing for many years, Neala now wants to take what she has studied, learnt and practised, and simplify it for anyone who thinks anything financial is too complicated and impossible to understand.

Introduction

Welcome to my new book, *What's Your Financial Game Plan? – The Workbook.*

Through the success of my debut book *What's Your Financial Game Plan?* many people have told me how much the book has encouraged them to handle their finances better and although all positive, the one thing that many of them mentioned would help was a toolkit to guide them through creating their own financial game plan.

I have read many finance books over the years but never really came across one that practically helped get a person from point A to point B financially. Now I know why I never came across a type of this book: they are very difficult to create and a lot of time, effort and thinking needs to go into it. I didn't want to bring out just any workbook. It was important that it was one that would genuinely help an individual or a family accomplish a realistic and sound financial game plan that was simple and yet easy to use and understand.

No beating around the bush

This toolkit gets straight to work to help you create your personal financial map. I have kept this workbook short and to the point – from the very first chapter we get started on the exercises.

By using the workbook, I hope you will:

❖ Know the true state of your personal finances.

❖ Be able to write up your game plan.

❖ Know how to fool-proof your money.

This book is designed to guide your knowledge of your finances through questions and exercises in order to help you know where you are currently and where to go from here.

The reason for writing my first book *What's Your Financial Game Plan?* was to encourage and empower the everyday person to have a game plan for their finances. Most people do not have a plan for their money; nor have they even thought about creating one. *What's Your Financial Game Plan?* covers such an approach and explains how you can either make your money work for you or against you.

This workbook takes things a step further and assists you in writing up your own plan. It is a manual of exercises and instructions that you can put into practice from what you learnt in the book. Even if you have not read my first book What's *Your Financial Game Plan?* you can still use this manual to help you with your personal finances.

If you have no financial goals at present, I hope that this workbook inspires you to put some in place. It is amazing how having a goal to work towards can help focus and motivate you.

❖ If you are in debt – *this workbook is for you.*

❖ If you are not in debt but are adrift with your finances – *this workbook will assist you.*

❖ You may want to grow your savings and investments and therefore need a game plan to help you utilise your money wisely – *this workbook applies to you.*

❖ You may be starting or thinking of starting your money-making journey – *this workbook is also for you.*

I have arranged the workbook so you can refer to the glossary at the back when you come across a name or phrase you do not understand. Words in the glossary are in SMALL CAPS throughout the book.

What you will need

You will need your **latest bank statements**, preferably for three to six months. If you have physical copies, great, otherwise you can either get a printout from your online banking, or machines in the bank will print them out for you.

You will also need your **utility bills** (council tax, electricity, gas, phone, water, etc.) and **information on any other expenses you incur regularly** (such as travel costs, your rent or mortgage payments, membership details or subscriptions, etc.)

Finally, you will need a **calculator**. I have kept the calculations basic and easy for you to follow but you will still need to have one to hand.

There are sections of the book where I have left blank spreadsheet templates and note areas – this is so that you can use the book as a real toolkit and fill it in as you go. I have made sure that this workbook can be used to write all your notes and, once you have worked through it, you will be able to see your full personal financial game plan. If you prefer to put this information on a spreadsheet on your computer or photocopy the pages, feel free to do that. I would recommend jotting down the points in the book – that way you can always refer back to it when writing or adjusting your future financial game plan.

Please remember this workbook is personal to you and will contain your private financial information. Therefore, I recommend keeping it in a safe place where only you can access.

One other point: please do not let bank statements, calculating numbers and figures put you off. I promise to make this as pain-free and as easy as possible, but it will still need your full concentration. **I would recommend when starting this process to aim to complete it within a certain time frame, otherwise you may forget what your notes meant and will have to figure out where you left off, which can be difficult.**

A final note to you – a financial game plan must be adaptable and flexible. We live in a fast-moving economy and even our financial situations are constantly changing for a variety of reasons– for example, because of a new job, a redundancy, increase in living costs, to name a few. An inflexible financial game plan can create more problems than help in your path to financial success. We tackle all of this in the following chapters.

NB: As we go through the exercises in this workbook, bear in mind each individual/family circumstance is different; therefore, it is up to you to do the relevant research and adjustments that best suit your needs and those of your family.

The information this book provides is to act as a guide only.

Finally, let's get started!!!

I hope you enjoy this workbook and find it useful. For more information, please follow me on my website **www.whatsyourfinancialgameplan.com**

Guidelines

Having GUIDELINES to govern my financial decision-making processes is something I personally know the importance of. They should really be part of a person's financial plan.

Through my own life experiences with money, and also through my years of conversations with people on their finances, I have come to the realisation that guidelines are an extremely important part of everyone's financial game plan.

Originally, my husband and I did not have a solid set of guidelines in place to help govern our financial approach, even though we knew where we were going financially. After some time, by not having these what I call 'enlighteners', we realised that we frequently deviated from the course of our financial game plan. This was often to the detriment of our personal finances.

We needed guidelines to govern our decision-making process when it came to money.

To be honest, there were times when we made unwise financial decisions that could have been avoided if we originally had these guidelines in place. This can happen to anybody.

You may be asking 'What is a guideline?'

A guideline is a statement of principles put forward to set standards or in order to determine a course of action.

In other words, it is a set of principles that govern the course of action you want to take with your finances. It is recognising what you hold as important or that you do not want to compromise on.

As an example, a long time ago my husband and I decided to stay out of debt, i.e. we would have no credit cards, loans, overdraft, etc. except for a mortgage. We had initially spoken about it years ago, but after time passed we had compromised a little here, a little there: took out a credit card, played the so-called credit card game, then we took out a loan… until one day, upon doing our annual financial outlook, I realised we had compromised on our principles and we hadn't even realised it had happened.

In order to avoid this happening again in the future, we discussed a set of guidelines, wrote them up, saved them on our computer and printed them out so that we would not forget. As a family, we aim to revisit these guidelines every year and see if they have been adhered to or need re-adjusting to fit our current financial situation. This has proven successful for us.

I aim to start your thinking processes so that, as you complete each exercise in the following chapters, you will be able to see in the context of your finances, what you want and like, and what you don't want and dislike.

We will revisit this section again at the very end of the book as by then, you should have a very clear idea of what sort of guidelines you will want to put in place along the path to your financial success.

I have a few exercises for you to do right now that you can then finalise when you reach the end of this book.

Exercise A: Guidelines

Here are some examples of guidelines to start with. Please remember it is really about what is important to you and what <u>you</u> do not want to compromise on that you need to consider. Examples could include:

- ❖ Spending quality time with family.

- ❖ Never using a credit card.

- ❖ Paying off a credit card fully at the end of the month.

- ❖ Putting money aside regularly to develop a peace-of-mind fund.

- ❖ Adding extra money monthly to paying off the mortgage.

- ❖ Not willing to take too many financial risks.

- ❖ Giving to charity.

Write down some points on the next page that you can think of that you would like to use as a guideline? Jot them down here as a starting point. We will repeat this exercise at the very end of the book as your thinking may have changed by then.

These points must be pivotal to what you stand for and what you will not compromise on.

It is good to write up your guidelines and review them annually.

I would recommend printing them out, laminating them and putting the sheet somewhere you can see it daily. Your guidelines govern your financial outlook and the decisions that you make now and in the future.

My Guidelines

My Guidelines

The Now

Your Income and Expenditure Position

Welcome to the first chapter of what I call the short and simple, yet effective way of creating your personal financial game plan.

> *A financial game plan is a document that details how you are going to move from your current financial situation to a more successful financial state in the future.*

Your financial plan should also be adaptable and flexible to your personal circumstances and the general economy you live in.

We will be jumping straight into the exercises. It may seem difficult, but don't worry. The most difficult part of this workbook is in this first chapter. This hard part is working out what your current financial situation is. Some people may already know this and, fortunately for them, they can breeze through this exercise. However, for the majority of us, this is the point where it will mean concentration and effort. Please understand: doing this exercise is definitely worth it. Please do not get put off by what I am saying – if we get this section right, then the rest of the book will be easier for you to complete. If you persevere, you and your finances will be VERY happy for it.

If you find it hard doing all these exercises, I would recommend that you ask someone professional for help, or visit organisations that specialise in this area. You can also visit my website www.whatsyourfinancialgameplan.com as I have put up information, explanations and even video seminars that can help you with your financial game plan.

INCOME AND EXPENDITURE STATEMENT

A statement to measure an individual's financial performance over a specific period of time. A person's financial performance is assessed by creating a summary of how that person incurs their income and expenses. It also shows the profit or loss incurred over a specific period, typically a month, quarter or year.

What is your current financial position?

In order to put together an Income and Expenditure Statement, we will need to know what your monthly income and expenses are. It is important that you spend some time on getting this section right.

This is the part where you will need:

- ❖ your bank statements;

- ❖ all your latest wage slips or information about your income;

- ❖ bills that you pay, e.g. mobile phone, food, travel, etc.

INCOME

Cash or cash equivalents received from work (wage or salary after tax), capital (interest or profit), or land (rent).   —www.businessdirectory.com

---

Exercise B: Your Income

Write up a list of all your INCOME (that is, any money that comes in; e.g. salary, any government benefits you receive, etc.) in the space on the next page.

Make sure you jot down your income calculations so that you remember it in the future.

For this exercise, and for the sake of simplicity, please enter monthly figures. Here are some simple calculations you can use if you get paid weekly, fortnightly or on a four-weekly basis. We want to keep the spreadsheet as simple as possible so we will be using monthly spreadsheets and figures.

It is good to keep a record of how you came to a certain figure, especially for future reference. That is why I have put these spaces throughout the book – for you to keep a record of your calculations and the method used, rather than scratching your head later trying to work out how you came to these figures/amounts.

For those of you who need to calculate a monthly amount:

- ❖ **Weekly** wage or salary x 52 then ÷ 12

e.g. £300 x 52÷12 = £1,300 per month

- ❖ **Fortnightly** wage or salary x 26 then ÷ 12

- ❖ **Four-weekly** wage or salary x 13 then ÷12

Your Income

EXPENSE (EXPENDITURE)

An expense is a cost that is 'paid', usually in exchange for something of value. Buying food, clothing, furniture or a car is often referred to as an expense.

Exercise C: Your Expenses

Write up a list of all your EXPENSES (what you spend money on.)

Jot down what the expense is, the amount and the calculation method if you had to use one. Remember the daily, weekly or quarterly costs need to be re-calculated into a monthly figure.

For **this** particular exercise, please note that any **monthly savings or investments** outgoings is not considered an expense and therefore should not be included in this Income and Expenditure spreadsheet. We tackle these topics later on in the book. An expense in this exercise is a **payment.**

You will need to spend some time getting this right. When you write up a list of all your expenses, include everything: daily (e.g. lunch and pocket money), weekly (e.g. weekly travel expenses), monthly (e.g. utility bills, rent or MORTGAGE, student LOAN), quarterly (costs occurring or appearing at three month intervals; e.g. telephone bills), and yearly costs (e.g. insurance costs and road tax). It is imperative that you give this the attention it deserves. If you have a partner, I would recommend doing this together. The main point of this exercise is to leave no stone unturned.

To calculate a monthly amount:

❖ **Weekly** expense x 52 then ÷ 12

e.g. £27 x 52÷12 = £117 per month

❖ **Quarterly** expense x 4 then ÷ 12

❖ **Yearly** expense ÷ 12

Your Expenses

Here is an example of an INCOME AND EXPENDITURE STATEMENT. This example is taken from my book *What's Your Financial Game Plan?* and it is just to give you an idea of what the spreadsheet should look like. This particular one is not very detailed, but I am sure you get the idea of what I am trying to portray.

Monthly income and expenditure statement example

DETAILS	£
Income	
Salary (after tax)	1,000.00
Total Income	1,000.00
Expenditure	
Rent	400.00
Transportation Cost	200.00
Loans & Credit Cards	195.00
Utilities	180.00
Food	125.00
Entertainment	100.00
Total Expenditure	1,200.00
Loss	**(200.00)**

All households are different; therefore, you must make the INCOME AND EXPENDITURE SPREADSHEET that follows relevant to you. We will now pull in all our income figures and all our expenses figures from the previous exercises and slot them into our Income and Expenditure template.

Utilities mentioned in the spreadsheet listed are everyday necessity costs to the home. UTILITIES cover water bills, electricity and gas bills, telephone services and other essentials.

For the context of this book, **Transportation Costs** are all the costs necessary for running and maintaining a car. These costs cover car payments, insurance, TAXES, fuel and maintenance costs. TRANSPORTATION COSTS also include all other costs associated with any travel you and your family undertake, e.g. using the buses, trains, etc.

Entertainment cover costs e.g. subscriptions costs (i.e. magazines, newspapers, films), memberships (i.e. for golf or gym etc.) and any other costs that may fall into this category that is specific to you.

These spreadsheet headings should give you an idea of how to fill in the following Income and Expenditure template.

Note: On the following pages, I have put in a detailed Income and Expenditure spreadsheet template to make it applicable to everyone. However, you only need to use the sections that are relevant to you.

As I stated earlier, once you get this section correct and have completed it, the rest of the book becomes much easier.

Exercise D: Income and Expenditure Spreadsheet

Income

CATEGORY	MONTHLY AMOUNT	NOTES
INCOME:		
Wages/Salary after tax		Count wages for working members of the household
Government/State Benefits		Make a separate list of each benefit coming into the household.
Any other income		
Total INCOME:		

Expenses

CATEGORY	MONTHLY AMOUNT	NOTES
EXPENSES:		
HOME:		
Mortgage or Rent		If you have more than one of each of these categories, list them separately and put the totals in the relevant boxes. Make a note of these on the pages at the end of the chapter for future reference.
Building insurance		
Contents insurance		
House tax		
Council tax		
Service charges		
Other home charges		
Total HOME:		
TRANSPORTATION:		
Car purchase payments		Make sure you do these calculations for each vehicle cost you are responsible for.
Insurance		
Tax		
Servicing /MOT		

(Continued on next page)

Other transportation used (bus, tube, train, etc.)		
Total TRANSPORTATION:		
UTILITIES:		
Electricity		
Gas		
Water		
TV License		
Satellite/Cable		
Landline Telephone		
Mobile Telephone		Include all mobile phone costs you are responsible for
Broadband/Wi-Fi		
Other Utilities		
Total UTILITIES:		
FOOD:		
Monthly grocery bill		
Lunches, snacks, etc.		Include all members of the family that incur these costs in this figure.
Meals out, takeaways		

(Continued on next page)

Other food		
Total FOOD:		
ENTERTAINMENT:		
Memberships (gym, golf, etc.)		List each subscription/activity separately for these sections and then total the amount to enter into the box. Make a note of these on the pages at the end of the chapter for future reference.
Subscriptions (magazines, newspapers, films)		
Children's activities (Scouts, ballet, drama, etc.)		
Other Entertainment		
Total ENTERTAINMENT:		
DEBT PAYMENTS		
Credit/Store Cards		Add the monthly payment amounts for each credit/ store card
Bank Loan		
Hire Purchase		

(Continued on next page)

Other loans		
Total Monthly DEBT PAYMENTS		
OTHER UNSPECIFIED EXPENSES		
List anything not mentioned above, e.g. pet cost, health insurance etc.		
Total UNSPECIFIED Expense		
TOTAL EXPENSES		
PROFIT OR LOSS		

Remember that savings and investments costs are not included in this spreadsheet, we tackle these topics later in the book.

Wow! Give yourself a big pat on the back… we have completed the most difficult chapter; it now gets better from here. Well done.

Your Calculations

Financial Position: Your Present Outlook

In this chapter and the chapters to follow, we will be learning how to analyse the Income and Expenditure spreadsheet you have just completed and how to adjust and adapt this spreadsheet into a positive financial game plan.

Now that you have completed the exercise in chapter one, we need to figure out which financial position you fall into.

> ⁊ Ⳑ
>
> *There are four financial categories that individuals and families generally fall into.*
>
> 1. *Debt*
> 2. *Breakeven*
> 3. *Savings*
> 4. *Savings and Investments*

As I explain these terms further below, please make a note of which one applies to you. It should be quite clear which category you belong to, but if it is not then choose the one you feel most represents your true financial picture and use it as your starting guide position.

Here are further breakdowns of explanations of these terms for your understanding. It might be worth highlighting which one you belong to. You can use a highlighter or coloured pen to do this.

DEBT

Your **monthly** EXPENSES EXCEEDS **monthly** INCOME

Income < Expense = (Loss)

Your expenses exceed your income, leaving you in a loss position at the end of the month.

The brackets mean that it is a negative balance and therefore, in the context of this book, it is called debt.

e.g. Income = £1,000; Expense = £1,200

£1,000 – £1,200 = (£200)

BREAKEVEN

Your **monthly** INCOME EQUALS your **monthly** EXPENSES

Your expenses and your income are equal with a zero balance (or a close approximation to zero) on a monthly basis.

e.g. Income = £1,000; Expense = £1,000

£1,000 – £1,000 = 0

The balance above comes to zero, hence this is called breakeven.

SAVINGS

Your **monthly** INCOME IS GREATER THAN your **monthly** EXPENSES = SAVINGS
(otherwise known as profits)

Your income is greater than your expenses, leaving you with a profit position at the end of the month. This profit can be saved.

e.g. Income = £1,000; Expense = £900

£1,000 – £900 = £100

The £100 above represents a positive outcome or savings position. Some of you may have already been putting aside a monthly amount for savings. Your profit figure should then either be similar to your monthly savings figure or it will give a clearer picture of the amount available after expenses for savings.

SAVINGS AND INVESTMENTS

Your **monthly** INCOME IS MUCH GREATER THAN your **monthly** EXPENSES = SAVINGS & INVESTMENTS
(otherwise known as profits)

Your income is much greater than your expenses, leaving you with a savings and investment profit position at the end of the month.

e.g. Income = £1,000; Expense = £800

£1,000 – £800 = £200*

£100 = Savings
£100 = Investments

*The £200 above again represents a positive outcome; however, for the purpose of this book, we call it the savings/investment position. As stated earlier, some of you may already be putting aside money on a month-by-month basis for the savings and savings/investment categories. Your profit figure should then *either* be similar or a close approximation to your monthly savings and investment monthly amounts *or* it now gives you a clearer picture of the amount available after expenses for you to start saving/investing. This will be further explained as we continue with these exercises.

I am hoping most of you now have an understanding to which financial category you fit into. It may not feel pleasant for some of you to realise the category that represents you, but the whole purpose of this book is to help you create a better financial game plan so that your money can start working for you. The great news is that you are facing your finances head on and things can change from here.

Notes

Write down which category you fall into for later comparison.

As a general rule of thumb, if you fall into the debt category (where your expenses are greater than your income on a month-by-month basis), then it may be more difficult to move you on from that situation to a more positive one. It can be done, but I want to prepare you that it may require some cutting back or adjustments to bring your finances to first a breakeven and then a savings or savings/investment category.

For those of you who are in a breakeven, savings, or even savings/investment grouping, please do not become comfortable at this stage. What we want is to get your money working for you and to fool-proof your plan so things remain positive in the future. There is still work to be done to get to the financial game plan that you want or desire.

Finance Report Card

Your Credit History

Now you have the information from the last two chapters, and generally know which financial category you fit into, we now want to take this information one step further to reinforce your findings. This is where you get to know the true state of your financial situation at this moment in time. Even though your monthly INCOME AND EXPENDITURE STATEMENT is one piece of the puzzle and gives a good view of where you are at financially, we can get an even clearer view by working out this next piece of the jigsaw.

Why your credit report is important

Over the past decade, a credit report has become a fundamental piece of information in a person's financial outlook. A credit report is a collection of information about the way an individual handles debt. It includes data about how much debt they've accumulated, how they pay their bills, where they live, where they work, whether they've filed bankruptcy or have had a County Court Judgment. A COUNTY COURT JUDGMENT (CCJ) is a type of court order issued against someone in England, Wales and Northern Ireland if they fail to repay money they owe.

This report has become an important document in a person's financial history and may be important for their future financial success. Your credit report usually contains a lot of information about you.

The next piece in the jigsaw is therefore to find out what your CREDIT REPORT says about your financial situation.

Here are some definitions below:

> **CREDIT HISTORY or CREDIT REPORT**
>
> A record of an individual's past borrowing and repaying, including late payments and bankruptcy.

CREDIT SCORE

This represents the creditworthiness of a person. Lenders use credit scores to determine who qualifies for a LOAN, at what INTEREST RATE and what CREDIT LIMITS.

Not everyone reading this workbook will have access to a credit report. That is okay; you can still continue on with the exercises. A credit report/score really just helps solidify our full financial outlook for those of us with a recorded financial history. As an example, young adults in college or university may not necessarily have a financial history or credit report.

You can get this information from a credit scoring agency on a monthly or even annual basis. Using a free site such as www.noddle.co.uk in the U.K., you can get a full credit report with score and history. There are other sites you can use such as Experian or Equifax but, at the time of writing this book, www.noddle.co.uk was the only site offering a free report that you can look at regularly.

In Britain, your credit score can be displayed in a variety of ways. It could be presented as a single number between 0 and 1,000 or a score between 1 and 5. Depending on what this number is (compared to the top and bottom figures of the scale) will affect the rate of interest you will pay for borrowing. The higher your credit score on that scale, the better your credit rating. A high credit score means that you will pay a lower interest on any money you borrow or owe.

A low credit score means you could end up paying huge amounts of interest on any money you borrow or owe. Some people may not have a good score because they do not borrow money or have any regular payments coming from their bank account. In that situation, having a low score does not necessarily mean your finances are in a bad state.

It is important to protect your credit score; otherwise you will be wasting money paying unnecessary interest charges. The companies listed earlier in this chapter are the most reputable and recognised in the U.K for checking credit scores and can also assist you by giving advice in making your credit score better. I definitely advise speaking to them.

I now recommend that you sign up to one of these credit scoring websites and find out what your credit report says and what your credit score is. Please ensure it is a reputable and safe credit scoring website.

Notes
Write down your credit score and any other points you think relevant from your credit report, including any County Court Judgment or alerts.

I recommend checking this figure at least annually as it can help save a lot of money if you ever need to borrow.

I know there are quite a few people who think that checking their credit score will affect their credit rating. This is a myth. It is only when you apply to borrow money – e.g. a loan, overdraft, mortgage – or apply for something like a new phone that this **may** adversely affect your credit rating, but only if done too often.

Be aware that there are two types of enquiries that can occur on your credit report: **hard enquiries** and **soft enquiries**. Generally speaking, only hard enquiries can negatively affect your credit score.

HARD ENQUIRIES usually occur when a financial institution – such as a lender or credit card issuer – checks your credit report when making a lending decision. This commonly takes place when you apply for a loan, credit card or mortgage and you typically have to authorise them.

SOFT ENQUIRIES usually occur when a person or company checks your credit report as part of a background check. Examples can include employer background checks, getting pre-approved for credit offers and checking your own credit score. Unlike hard enquiries, a soft enquiry may occur without your permission. However, they won't generally affect your credit score

Note: At the time of writing this workbook, the companies listed in the Useful Information section at the back are the most reputable and recognised in the U.K. for checking credit scores and can provide more information on soft and hard credit enquiries.

Conclusion

We have now completed two major exercises regarding your current (at this present time) personal financial situation. We have drawn up your INCOME AND EXPENDITURE STATEMENT and we now have your CREDIT REPORT.

Before moving on to the next section of this book, please take the time to really analyse these two reports. Also, look at your bank statement and see how you spend money, and what your money is being spent on. The next chapter will delve a little deeper into the findings from these exercises.

Notes

Add any notes on the next page that you may consider from looking at the INCOME AND EXPENDITURE STATEMENT and CREDIT REPORT.

Financial Position: Debt Analysis

Stressed and Depressed

I recommend that you do not skip this chapter, even if you have not found yourself in the DEBT category, because we will be looking at spending behaviours and how they affect our finances, before working through exercises to counter any negative habits. Even though your finances may be looking healthy, you could possibly have some habits that may not be good for the overall plan you have for your financial future. It is important that you do not skip forward, but try and complete all the exercises in this book.

Let's now delve into the chapter. We will first tackle the debt scenario.

DEBT

Your **monthly** EXPENSES EXCEEDS **monthly** INCOME

Income < Expense = (Loss)

Your expenses exceed your income, leaving you in a loss position at the end of the month.

The brackets mean that it is a negative balance and therefore, in the context of this book, it is called debt.

e.g. £1,000 – £1,200 = (£200)

You should skip exercise E listed below if you do not fall into the Debt category

---

Exercise E: Your Debt

Write your monthly debt or shortfall here. You will find this information from the Income and Expenditure exercise you completed in Chapter 1 *The Now*.

I have a monthly shortfall of £_____

This number does not need to be exact – a close approximation will do. This figure may be subject to change month from month. That is why a close approximation or average will work.

In order to move forward from this position, especially if it is a month-on-month scenario, you need to be willing to put the effort in bringing this under control. If this is not tackled, most debt situations will compound.

Compounding

What do I mean by compounding?

As an example, let's look at an avalanche – how does it start? It starts as a small mass of snow that gains momentum as it continues sliding down the mountain, getting massively bigger and bigger and moving faster the closer it gets to the bottom. This is the same with debt. It starts off as non-existent. It gets to be a small problem, but as time goes on it can quickly develop into a massive problem. This is called COMPOUNDING.

When the debt burden becomes so large, it inevitably begins to progressively increase interest payments leading to greater debt. Suddenly a person is paying interest on top of interest on their debt. This leads to a rapid expansion of the interest payment on their debt.

This is why writing up a financial game plan is important to everyone who finds themselves in this category. For you, a positive financial game plan is getting into a breakeven position before moving onto a savings position. I recommend that we move systematically from one to the next, otherwise you may really struggle if we go too fast and there is a danger that you could go back to your old ways even worse than before. My approach is one step at a time. Remember, Rome was not built in a day.

Spending habits

A habit is an acquired behaviour pattern regularly followed, sometimes without knowing that you are doing it – e.g. a habit of going to bed early.

Sometimes our spending habits have been developed through the years and we may not be aware that we have them because we do them unconsciously. Usually this can have an impact on the success or failure of our financial game plan. Therefore, analysing money behaviour patterns and re-cultivating good money habits is an important step to having financial success.

We will now look at habits in the context of your money – both good and bad. It is time to get practical in creating our new financial game plan; but first, we need to really analyse how we view and handle money.

Generally speaking, habits can start from very early on in life; they could be good habits or bad habits. It is worth studying your spending habits to see what they are like.

If your spending is not done in an orderly manner with thought and consideration, these habits can generally lead to financial chaos/problems that can sometimes take years to recover from.

Exercise F: Habits

In this exercise, we aim to try and see which habits are good and should be encouraged to grow, and which habits are not good and need to change if we want our money working for us. Consider each question and either put a ring around the most appropriate answer, or answer the questions on the notepaper under the question.

Ask yourself:

1. When it comes to spending:

    a. I spend frivolously without checking if I can afford the item/service.

    b. I don't like to spend money and prefer to save my money.

    c. I spend only what I can afford.

2. Do I buy items now and worry about how to pay for them later?

    Yes/No or Sometimes (Circle the appropriate answer)

3. If 'yes' or 'sometimes', what types of items/services do I purchase and then worry about how to pay for them later. Try remembering a recent time when this would have occurred.

4. What are my family members' spending habits like?

    Individuals knowingly or unknowingly tend to pick up habits from family members. We can sometimes follow the way our mother, father or even our grandparents spend or save money.

5.   Do I think my spending habits are manageable?

         Yes, No or Maybe? (Circle the appropriate answer)

Give reasons:

_____

_____

_____

_____

_____

6.   Do I ignore my post/mail for fear of outstanding bills?

         Yes, No or Maybe? (Circle the appropriate answer)

7.   From this exercise, what sort of spending habits do you think you have and do you think they are sustainable? Will some of these habits lead to financial success in the future or will they hinder you?

What are you going to do about them?

_____

_____

_____

_____

_____

_____

Please note: It generally takes 21 days for habits to be created. If you adjust or change some of your habits, and keep practising them for one month, you may be able to form some new habits that can benefit your financial game plan.

Personally, I believe a two- to three-month period to be a more realistic timeframe when adjusting or changing financial habits. Therefore, if after 21 days you are not seeing progress in your new habits, keep practising them and then review after two or three months.

Tackling debt

Next, we need to look at the types of debts you may have accumulated over the years and the amount of money/balance attached to each. The main types of debts people can incur include:

Short-term debt

- ❖ credit card debts
- ❖ loans, payday advances
- ❖ money you would have borrowed from family or friends

Long-term debt

- ❖ buying a car on credit
- ❖ student loan

Other forms of debt

- ❖ bank overdraft facility
- ❖ mortgage

You now need to find out how much debt you as an individual or a family have outstanding at this present time.

Debt Summary spreadsheet

Here is an example of the next exercise you will need to complete (the notes are on the next page). For this example, we will say this person brings home a salary of £1,400 after tax per

TYPE OF DEBT	Interest Charged on Debt or APR	Balance Outstanding	Monthly Payment Amount
Mortgage	5%	£100,000	£585
Loans	6.5%	£7,500	£147
Credit Card(s)	Interest-free for 12 months	£4,500	£100
Overdraft	12%	£895	£18.87
Money owed to Family or Friends	0	£5,000	£70
Total Debt		£117,895	£920.87

month.

The Balance Outstanding column = £117,895 total debt at this period in time.

The total monthly payments column = £920.87 of debt repayment a month.

Therefore, what this tells me is that every month this person pays £920.87 in debt repayments.

If the person in this example brings home a salary of £1,400 per month, about 66% (£920÷£1,400 x 100) of this person's salary is going towards debt payments. This does not leave much money (£479.13) for other bills, including food, transport and day-to-day living.

APR (Annual Percentage Rate)

APR is a term you will see on several different lending products including mortgages, credit cards and loans. Short for Annual Percentage Rate, it is basically **how much your borrowing will cost over the period of an average year, over the duration of your debt.**

The APR can be calculated in several ways depending on the terms of the loan, but the basic formula is:

For a £1,000 loan with an APR of 10% to be paid back in twelve months:

The amount of the APR over a year: £100 (10%) yearly interest charge for the £1,000 loan.

The monthly interest amount would be £100 ÷ 12 months = £8.33 monthly interest payment.

Remember we must add the actual loan monthly payment £1,000 ÷ 12 = £83.33.

Therefore, the loan amount (£83.33) + the interest amount (£8.33) = £91.66. This figure is your monthly payment.

At the end of the loan, you would have paid back £91.66 x 12 months = £1,100.

Please remember the calculation can be more complex than this depending on the terms of agreement made with your lending institution.

I do <u>not</u> need you to calculate the APR for all your outstanding debts – it is the legal requirement of each lending institution to calculate this for you. However, I do believe it is good for you to have an understanding of how this formula is worked out. The majority of the time, the monthly loan repayment amount is fixed and you can get this information from your bank statement or your original loan agreement.

Overdraft facilities and sometimes credit cards can become trickier to calculate. I would recommend doing the basic formula and putting in a monthly figure rather than leaving the space blank, or call your lenders and ask them for a rough monthly estimate figure that you can use.

With the next exercise, we really want to be as accurate as possible. However, please remember if you give it your best guess either using a calculation or calling the lenders, this is okay. The main thing is that we know this debt exists and we have accounted for it in our calculations. Even I make best guesses with figures when I don't have the answers. Do not let this put you off.

Exercise G: Debt Summary Spreadsheet

Fill in the table below to see what your main debts are. Again, this exercise is for everyone — even those who do not fall into the debt category — as most of us have some form of debt or another.

TYPE OF DEBT	Interest Charged on Debt or APR	Total Balance Outstanding	Monthly Payment Amount
Mortgage			
Loans			
Student loan			
Credit card(s)			
Overdraft			

(Continued on next page)

Hire purchase			
Money owed to family or friends			
Other debt			
Total amount of debt			

Ask yourself this question: What percentage of my monthly salary does my monthly debt payments make up?

After completing this particular exercise, and when you combine it with your Income & Expenditure statement and your credit report file, some of you may find this hard to look at. I have been there myself and have known individuals and couples who have done similar exercises. The results can be a shock, and it takes time to digest the information.

It isn't until you see the full picture put together that you can fully comprehend what needs to be done. If, when looking at these statements combined, you realise that your financial situation looks unhealthy, it may be a good idea to seek professional help or guidance – such as reading books on how to get out of debt or, if in the U.K., contacting your local Citizens Advice Bureau.

Getting your finances under control can be done, but I won't mince words! It will take time and sometimes a lot of effort – but it is worth it. This book will help you look towards the future and plan for it.

Exercise H: Saving Money

Ask yourself 'What am I willing to give up that will save me money on a monthly basis? Or what can I cut down on?' Here are a few examples:

❖ Monthly gym membership – using the park to exercise.

❖ Cable television subscription– free package or free TV box set may be available.

❖ Cutting down on monthly grocery shopping. Have less takeaway food a month or no takeaway for a period of time.

❖ Recycle the current clothes in your wardrobe and have a treat of one article of clothing a month; or even denying yourself clothes shopping for a time (to help with this I find looking through my clothes closet and doing an inventory makes me realise I have clothes I can reuse).

❖ Look at your phone tariffs or package and see how you can reduce the costs. Do you need more than one phone or even the latest phone? You do not need to upgrade when upgrade is due……haggle or barter to reduce your costs.

❖ Is taking public transport cheaper than using your car?

❖ Is the current car you have too expensive to run, do you need to downsize?

❖ An even more difficult question may be: can you afford the mortgage or rent of your present home? Do you possibly need to downsize?

I know these are difficult questions, but even I ask them myself ever so occasionally to keep a check on my spending habits and ensure I am on track with my financial game plan.

List some of the things you think can cut back on or reduce the cost of.

Even if you are not *in* debt, your spending habits may still need some considerable improvements (we look at how to tackle these things later in the book) because at present they may be unsustainable and this is not good for your financial game plan. Even though you may be getting away with your spending now, these habits could turn your financial position into a debt situation in the future if you do not take full control.

During my research, I have discovered that 30% or more of people living in Western society live outside of their means: they spend more money than they earn. This is quite a large proportion of people.

Will you be one of these statistics, or are you willing to change your mindset and habits, and implement positive action that will lead you to a successful financial future?

Notes

Well, we are getting there. Stick with me — when you have a plan that is workable and that you can reasonably achieve at the end of this, things will start improving.

Financial Position: Breakeven Analysis

The Hidden Trap

This is where your monthly income meets your monthly expenditure, bringing you to a zero balance at the end of the month. Unfortunately, this leaves you with no remaining money at the end of the month but it has ensured all of your **monthly** bills are taken care of.

BREAKEVEN

Your **monthly** INCOME EQUALS your **monthly** EXPENSES
I emphasise the word *monthly*.

Your expenses and your income are equal with on average a zero balance on a monthly basis.

e.g. Income = £1,000; Expense = £1,000

£1,000 – £1,000 = 0

The balance above comes to zero, hence this is called breakeven.

It is quite good to know this information and to balance it so evenly, where income exactly equals expenditure. Quite a large proportion of people in our society today do not manage to do this.

I would like to repeat that the exercises in this section again apply to everyone, even those who are in a 'savings' or 'savings and investment' category. This section is important to everyone's financial game plan.

For this particular chapter, we will be looking at the breakeven analysis from two points of view.

1. People who are in a debt position and want (need) to move into a breakeven position.

2. People who are already in a breakeven or savings position.

Which one most applies to you from the above two points mentioned? Write it here:

_____

_____

People who are in a debt position and want (need) to move into a breakeven position

For those of you who are in a debt position, I would recommend taking a look at your recent INCOME AND EXPENDITURE STATEMENT and see where or what you can cut back on. Actually, everyone should do this particular exercise as it really helps to analyse spending habits.

It is imperative that you find areas of costs to reduce so that you can come into a breakeven position, otherwise your financial situation will continue to deteriorate. Remember the definition of debt compounding from the previous chapter? We want to avoid this. In the previous chapter, we started thinking about areas where we can reduce costs. Now we make it more practical by actually looking at these costs and how much we can reduce them by.

When looking to reduce certain costs where your credit will be checked, such as credit card bills, insurance costs, loans, mobile phone tariffs or mortgages, make sure you ask these companies whether they will be doing a HARD or a SOFT CREDIT SEARCH. Also, ask whether this search will negatively affect your credit rating. I would recommend getting in contact with a reputable credit rating agency if you are unsure or need further clarity. Your local Citizens Advice Bureau or the Credit Reference Agency can offer support in this area before going ahead with cost cutting in these particular sections.

Refer to Chapter 3, Finance Report Card *for more information on hard or soft credit searches.*

Please be aware that each individual circumstance is different therefore make sure you check the relevant sources for your own finances. This information is to act as a guide only.

The following exercise may also involve calling up the companies such as your gym, etc. to ask how you can reduce your bills – be it monthly, quarterly or even annually. List everything you can think of.

In this exercise, thoroughly go through your expense list from your INCOME AND EXPENDITURE STATEMENT – you will find this information from Chapter 1, *The Now* 'Your Income and Expenditure Position Exercise D'. See what areas you can realistically reduce to help to bring you into a breakeven position.

Exercise I: Expense Reduction Analysis

Expenses	Current monthly cost	Reduction	New monthly cost
Telephone – example	£45	£20	£25
Gym (going to walk daily)	£50	£50	£0
Money owed to family/friends			
Total Amount of Costs			

People who are already in a breakeven position

Getting your monthly income to cover all your monthly expenses is really good. BUT… it is not good enough.

Unfortunately, there are problems that arise with the breakeven analysis. For example, your washing machine breaking down, an emergency dental procedure or the car needing fixing, etc. are sudden and unexpected bills. Alternatively, normal yearly expenses that most people tend to forget to budget for are ONE-OFF EXPENSES. This is why I call them the **HIDDEN TRAP**.

> *There will always be unexpected costs or costs you forgot to budget for; therefore, everyone needs a monthly fund in their budget to cover these unforeseen or forgotten costs.*

Exercise J: Have you budgeted for everything?

What bills have you forgotten to budget for or that were unexpected? Examples can include yearly insurance, a birthday or a work colleague's leaving present, new software for your computer, or the car breaking down, car tax, etc.

Sometimes, we are under the impression that we are on top of our finances. However, on closer inspection and after time has passed, a clearer picture emerges and you realise you are not. Suddenly you can see that you need to take on debt in order to cover all your costs, which can then spiral out of control. If something is not done about this, then you can start falling into the debt category without realising it.

> *When there is no room to manoeuver your finances to pay anything extra, this can inadvertently lead to debt. For example, taking out a CREDIT CARD to clear an unexpected balance – as there is no room in your monthly income to pay for these costs.*

Has this ever happened to you?

Yes/No?   If so, when?

How do we avoid the HIDDEN TRAP? We introduce the miscellaneous fund to our monthly budget.

> **MISCELLANEOUS FUND**
>
> (Otherwise known as a rainy-day fund or a ONE-OFF-EXPENSE FUND)
>
> Can be defined as a fund for small, unbudgeted miscellaneous costs that arise in our day-to-day lives.

Exercise K: Miscellaneous Fund

Do you already have this fund in place?   Yes/No (Circle the appropriate answer)

A rainy-day fund can also be viewed as a **short-term, easily accessible, on-going fund**. It must either be in an **easy-access bank account** or **put aside in an envelope**, and **not locked away** in a SAVINGS ACCOUNT that you cannot quickly access when an emergency arises.

Do you have such a bank account in place?   Yes/No (Circle the appropriate answer)

If yes, why? (e.g. is most of your purchases done online rather than in a store.)

_____

_____

_____

_____

The envelope system is where you put a set amount of money aside monthly for certain categories such as food, shopping, eating out and other miscellaneous items. When the envelope money is gone then there is no more money left for that item category for the month.

Should you adopt the ENVELOPE SYSTEM?   Yes/No (Circle the appropriate answer)
If no, why not? (e.g. you go through cash quickly.)

_____

_____

_____

_____

My husband and I have adopted the envelope system for part of our MISCELLANEOUS FUND and find it works really well for us. It also means there are fewer transactions coming through our bank statement monthly because we pay for most of these costs by cash.

What method would you prefer to use: your bank account, the envelope system or would you prefer to use both?

_____

_____

Recommended percentage

An average recommendation for your rainy-day fund would be an amount ranging from 4% to 10% of your monthly salary after tax. This of course depends on your personal financial circumstances.

Every item we buy has a useful economic lifespan and will eventually need to be replaced or fixed. Your rainy-day fund covers such situations. It also covers things such as gifts (birthdays, weddings, anniversaries) we may need to buy for friends and family, small emergency bills that occasionally arise and many other situations that crop up day-to-day. Having this fund and letting it build in the months we do not use it, or starting over when we do use it all, is wise financial planning.

How much can you put into your miscellaneous fund each month?

What items/everyday expenses will your rainy-day fund be likely to cover? Making a list for now will help you to know and remember how to use this fund and the purpose for which it exists. Use the space on the next page.

Monitor your miscellaneous fund

If you do decide to put this fund into action, I would recommend monitoring it over a three-month period. It could be that you have not put in enough money and therefore have a shortfall (insufficient money to cover these expenses) in all three months. At this point, you should either consider increasing the monthly amount of money you put into this category or re-analyse it to see if you are spending wisely. **This fund should even itself out on a month-by-month basis.**

I must also stress that this does not necessarily mean we will always be on top of our finances by having this one-off expense fund. However, it ensures that a good foundation is laid. There are many times other unforeseen circumstances, such as needing a new car, can occur that throw us off guard. The one-off expense fund may or may not be able to help in such situations.

Notes

Financial Position: Savings Analysis

Peace of Mind

The savings position is the one position everyone should aim to achieve. Reaching this category can have a huge impact in having financial success, for it gives you something to work with for the future. I know that living in the society we have today and with the cost of living rising, it is difficult for many people to save. But with some deep thought and a bit of sacrifice here and there, we can achieve this. It will cost, but it pays off in the future.

For those of you who are in the debt or breakeven category, even if the savings category seems a far-off dream, please do not skip this chapter. I myself have been there, only being able to imagine what being in a savings category would feel like. The one thing I did was dream and hope to get there one day and that led me to handle my finances more effectively, which led to, YES, the savings category. I did not let my current/present situation dictate to me where I would be in the future. I got there and so can you.

The exercises in this chapter and all the following chapters may not seem relevant now, but they are important because they will give you something to aspire to. You do not necessarily need to do the full exercises, but do what you can and put in some figures that you can realistically afford in a few years' time. You have started the process to having a successful game plan…

…let's go all the way – no matter what your age or situation.

SAVINGS

Your **monthly** INCOME IS GREATER THAN your **monthly** EXPENSES = SAVINGS *(otherwise known as profits)*

Your income is greater than your expenses, leaving you with a profit position at the end of the month. This profit can be saved.

£1,000 – £900 = £100

The £100 above represents a positive outcome or Savings position. Some of you may have already been putting aside money monthly for savings and this profit figure should then either be similar to your monthly savings figure or it will give a clearer picture of the amount available after expenses for savings.

If you are already in the savings category, great job! Please keep reading though because this section will enlighten you on how to get a healthier savings position and not just having savings. Hopefully it will get you thinking.

> *Have you ever heard people say 'I save regularly, but it never seems to grow', or 'I keep tapping into my savings'? Well, after having conversations with a few people, I found that one of the main reasons for this is not defining what your funds are for.*

FUNDS

A fund is a sum of money saved or made available for a particular purpose.

How does a savings fund differ from a miscellaneous fund?

The **rainy-day expense (miscellaneous) fund** can be defined as a fund for small, miscellaneous costs that arise in our day-to-day lives. It is sometimes viewed as a short-term, easily available and accessible on-going fund.

A **savings fund** is for a longer-term outlook and for longer-term goals. The goal can be specific or general. A lot of people like to put aside money monthly in a savings fund for the simple purpose of having peace of mind.

Therefore, it is very important that we define what a savings fund is and why it exists. Otherwise, if it is ambiguous and not clear cut, it can lead to cracks in your financial game plan.

Exercise L: Reason For Your savings (1)

Have you defined why your savings exist?

      Yes/No (Circle the appropriate answer)

If yes, jot down your reasons/definition.

A savings fund is good for two reasons:

1. It helps a person develop the habit of putting aside money, which is very hard in today's lifestyle and society; and,
2. It gives them a peace of mind that is very valuable, especially in today's stressful and fast-paced environment.

Important: The savings fund should be planned for. Have a reason why your savings exist.

Most of the time, people aim to have three to six months of their monthly expenses saved. I would personally recommend this, simply for the peace of mind it brings to you.

You can also put aside savings for other uses. Some examples could be: taking a holiday, buying a car, saving for a deposit for a house, paying off an existing mortgage, for a wedding or honeymoon, financing a professional course, or for occasionally treating yourself to some sort of luxury. It really depends on you as to what you use the money for. Even if you do not have a purpose for saving or can't think of one, it is still a good habit to get into – putting aside money each month.

If the thought of defining what your savings is for is too much for you right now, please start with getting into the habit of saving and letting it grow and then maybe sometime in the future come back to this exercise. The main point really is to have the savings.

Exercise M: Reason For Your Savings (2)

Have you come up with reasons/ideas for your savings or future savings? Write them down here:

Again, saving funds can be broken down into different categories, some shorter term than others.

You can put your savings into different savings accounts – even with different banks – depending on your uses and access needs.

Some savings can be locked away with the bank for long periods, such as five to ten years. As an average rule of thumb, the longer you lock it away for, the higher the interest rates you receive.

Alternatively, some savings can be locked away for shorter time frames, such as three months to a year. However, they are not likely to get as good an interest rate as if they were locked away for a longer period.

Remember there are no hard or fast rules to saving. These are just guidelines that can give you direction and purpose depending on the goals you personally set.

> *It is important to understand that saving is not risk-taking and brings in little or no return.*

We cover risk-taking financial plans in the next chapter.

If you as an individual set your mind to SAVE, you can SAVE – no matter how big or small an amount.

What amount can you save?

Looking at your income and expenditure combined with the other exercises you did previously, ask yourself realistically: 'what amount can I save?' If you were in a debt position at the beginning of the book, you may have found extra money that can be saved after doing the cost cutting exercises.

There are some people who, after looking at their income and expenditure, realise they can save 10% of their salary a month. If you can save 10%, that is great!

£1,000 (monthly salary) × 10% (savings %) = £100!!

Some people can save more than 10%. If you can honestly save more than 10%, then that is even better.

There are then the people who would not be able to save 10% but they can definitely save something monthly. Start small; if it is 2% of your monthly income or 9% of your monthly income that goes into savings, this is still great news.

£1,000 (salary) × 2% (savings %) = £20!

£1,000 (salary) × 9% (savings %) = £90!

Unfortunately, some people cannot save because their expenditure is greater than their income. Hopefully the previous chapters would have helped steer your finances in the right direction.

Exercise N: How Much Can You Save?

How much can you save per month? Or what percentage of your salary can you save?

Work out your calculations:

Fixed savings vs. percentage savings

You can either save a **fixed** monetary amount on a monthly basis (e.g. saving £100 every month) or save a **percentage** (%) of your monthly salary (e.g. 10%).

Most of us would be familiar with the FIXED RULE APPROACH as it is commonly used and quite straightforward to start, easy to set up with our banks and simple to maintain. This way, the same amount is saved every month or every year regardless of any increase or decrease in your income. It is simple and easy.

Some of us may recognise the PERCENTAGE RULE APPROACH, which can be technical and not as easy to maintain.

The benefit of using this approach is that when your salary increases or you get additional income, like a BONUS or monetary gift, you can easily apply the percentage rule and save money from these sources also.

Comparatively, if you save a fixed amount monthly then it does not matter when additional income comes in or what that amount is. The fixed rule approach is inflexible to increases or decreases in income, whereas a percentage amount is adaptable to these situations.

Look at the example on the next page. Don't forget, this money must be put in a safe place such as a savings account.

Which one will you want to introduce: fixed or percentage? Remember it is whatever works BEST for you.

	Income	Fixed amount per month	Percentage amount (10%)
June	£1,000	£100	£100
July	£900	£100	£90
August	£1,200	£100	£120
September	£1,250	£100	£125
October	£1,000	£100	£100
November	£1,350	£100	£135
December	£1,000	£100	£100
Total savings		**£700**	**£770**

Using the fixed rule is easy to apply and we can set a guaranteed monthly deduction of £100 with our bank.

The percentage rule is not as easy to apply, especially when our income fluctuates, but it guarantees our savings increase with our income, be it from bonuses, promotion or monetary gifts.

Saving should be a habit we all build into our lives.

Where will you put your savings?

Sometimes it is good to put it where it is more difficult for you to access this money immediately, especially if you recognise you may want to tap into it against your plan or have done this in the past with previous savings.

Alternatively, it might be more beneficial for you to put your money into an instant-access or short-term savings account if you have a more immediate goal for this money and feel you can remain in control of it.

Only you can know which of these is best for you, so make sure you put the proper measures in place to safeguard this money, and use it for what it is intended for. You alone will know what your financial strategy is after fully using this workbook.

Should you lock your savings away or keep it in a flexible account? What method would suit you best?

Notes

Financial Position: Savings and Investments Analysis

Relieved and Thankful

A good man leaves an inheritance to his children's children. (Proverbs 13:22, NKJV)

> *As individuals and families, we must think of our finances from a long-term perspective. The society we live in today would have us think in the short term, especially with regards to our money.*

Spending is actively encouraged, but putting aside money and planning for the future is not really promoted. **My aim in this chapter is to highlight how we must prepare for growing old and retiring**, and possibly even think of providing a starting block for our children and grandchildren as the proverbs above describes.

Think how wonderful it would be if you were to systematically grow your savings and investments – have you ever imagined how your children or grandchildren would feel if you were to help them pay for their schooling or even be able to help them buy a home. What joy would that bring you?

Therefore, I am aiming to focus your mind on having a plan for your personal money, and growing your money into savings and investments are an important part of that plan.

If you have skipped any of the previous chapters, I would recommend going through them before starting here; otherwise there may be cracks in your financial plan without you being aware they are there. The previous chapters help you recognise and mend those cracks.

SAVINGS AND INVESTMENTS

Your **monthly** INCOME IS MUCH GREATER THAN your **monthly** EXPENSES = SAVINGS & INVESTMENTS
(otherwise known as profits)

Your income is much greater than your expenses, leaving you with a savings and investment profit position at the end of the month.

e.g. Income = £1,000; Expense = £800

£1,000 – £800 = £200
£100 = Savings
£100 = Investments

The £200 above again represents a positive outcome, but for the purpose of this book we call it the savings/investment position. As we discussed in earlier chapters, some of you may already be putting aside money on a month-by-month basis for these two categories. Your **profit** figure from the Income and Expenditure exercise in Chapter 1, *The Now* should either be similar or a close approximation to your current monthly savings and investment amounts or it will give you a clearer picture of the amount you have available for them after expenses.

The £100 for savings represents the savings fund from the previous chapter. The £100 for investment funds will be used for our investing strategy. I have kept these two amounts simple in order to emphasise the point of the book. You will have to work out what your own monthly savings amount should be and what your monthly investment amount should look like.

Are you in this category? Yes/No_____

Would you like to be in this category?

Many of us aim to get to this category. There are some of us who are quite happy to stay in the savings category, and that is fine. However, I would still recommend reading this section as there is something to be learnt from each chapter. There may be some of you who already follow this savings/investment strategy where you have money put aside for both savings and investments. Hopefully, after reading this chapter, you will have a more solid idea of how to handle your money when it comes to investing.

Defining wealth

The Oxford English Dictionary defines WEALTH as 'Possessing well-being, being happy, comfortable, or having an abundance of valuable possessions or money'.

For me personally, wealth really is all about handling your money wisely – thinking about both the here and now and the future, with the aim of getting the best out of both. There is no hard and fast rule. It depends on the goals you set out for yourself when you think about wealth creation. It could be being debt free, with your mortgage and car paid off. If this is what gives you comfort and peace of mind then, when you achieve that, you are wealthy.

Exercise O: Thinking About Wealth

What is your personal definition of wealth?

What would you like to do with your wealth?

Your wealth goals should be realistic along with optimistic. To me, this is what true wealth is all about. It is not about the fancy cars and big houses, it is more about the peace of mind and comfort that comes from handling your finances well.

Remember, wealth is what you make of it.

The truth is it takes effort and sacrifice to acquire and grow investments, especially if you do not come from a wealthy background or are not left a fortune in someone's will. To make and grow investments will require discipline, dedication, sacrifice and some effort.

Exercise P: Character Traits

Circle the character traits that you think you already have:

Disciplined	Prudent	Determined	Focused
Dedicated	Good with numbers	Risk-taker	Calculated
Hard Worker	Quick Learner	Patient	Can recognise a good opportunity
Persistent	Adaptable to change	Teachable	Researches information

---

These are just a few traits that can help you along the way to growing your money and investments. Not all will apply, but having a few of these qualities will definitely help in the investing process.

For the average Joe Bloggs – meaning you and me – growing our money and investments will be a process built on discipline and hard work. Are you up for the challenge or have I put you off?

In previous chapters, we saw the introduction of the MISCELLANEOUS FUND – a fund for small miscellaneous expenses that occur in our everyday lives. We then looked at the purpose of the SAVINGS FUND, which is more of a peace-of-mind or longer-term fund, and we stated that these savings should be planned for. Now we will discuss the INVESTMENT FUND.

AN INVESTMENT FUND

A fund used solely and specifically for investing. An individual puts money aside from their salary into this fund for investing or until they are ready to invest.

෴

This is what I call the risk-taking fund........because any form of investing involves taking RISKS.

In order to take risks, I do believe we need to be prepared for them. Therefore, before we go into the investing arena, we plan and save for it.

When it comes to the investment fund, as a general guideline many experts such as financial advisors recommend using the 10% rule for making and growing wealth. That means having a 10% goal for SAVINGS and a 10% goal for investment. You then live off the remaining 80% of your salary, which should also include a RAINY-DAY FUND.

This can be quite difficult for many of us as sometimes there is no room in our finances to cater for this. Some people are so determined they are willing to take drastic measures to get their monthly budget to cater for this 10% rule. Are you willing to be one of these individuals?

Exercise Q: Sacrifices

What are you willing to, or CAN you, sacrifice to get to this monthly budget position?

These are very hard questions you need to ask yourself. If you have a family, you also need to make sure that they are willing and able to make these necessary adjustments.

Keep in mind the 10% guideline we spoke about earlier, but I would recommend introducing some flexibility into this equation. If you cannot afford 10% of your monthly salary, then introduce what you can afford. Is it 5% or 7% or even 3%? For me, it starts somewhere. Yes, the 10% parameter has a proven track record, but start with what you can realistically afford and maybe in the future you can work up to 10%.

Please remember, when doing these exercises and implementing these changes to your finances, to consider family members and whether they are also willing to make these adjustments. It is worth having this discussion with everyone to ensure that they are on board with cutting back or sacrificing now for the benefit of later. This is why agreed guidelines play an important role here. As an example, a husband or wife may not be in agreement over making these cutbacks now for the benefit of later. Family discussions play a crucial role.

The most important thing though, is to ensure you also have savings and a miscellaneous fund. I am sure that after reading the previous chapters, you understand why.

Investing

Let us now define INVESTING.

INVESTING

Putting money into financial or non-financial vehicles and instruments that have some degree of risk in the hope of seeing the money grow significantly over time.

FINANCIAL VEHICLES

Financial instruments whose value is determined directly by the financial markets. These vehicles can include investing in the stock market, e.g. via shares, bonds, ETFs (Exchange Traded Funds) or unit trusts.

NON-FINANCIAL VEHICLES

Investments that do not deal with financial goods or services that individuals or businesses can invest in and ideally, grow their money. These can include running your own small business or going into partnership with another business. It can be investing in an already existing business or it can be investing in property, either commercial or residential, land, jewellery or art, etc.

Exercise R: Investing

Do you currently have any investments?   Yes/No (Circle the appropriate one)

What are they?

How much do you currently have invested?

For FINANCIAL VEHICLES, this should include any ISA accounts, shares, pensions, etc. For NON-FINANCIAL VEHICLES, note down how much you have invested in your business, land/property, etc.

Compounding

Definition of compounding for growing investments:

> **COMPOUNDING**
>
> The ability of an asset to generate earnings. These earnings are then reinvested in order to generate their own earnings. An example can be if you reinvest any profits you make from your current investments listed above.

COMPOUNDING here refers to generating earnings from previous earnings such as interest on interest. This is one of the main principles successful people use to make wealth. Reinvesting earnings into your investments, after a time, multiplies into wealth.

Exercise S: Compounding

Have you already implemented this system where you reinvest your **interest** income received back into your investments?

Yes/No (Circle the appropriate one)

What are they? Please list here.

Have you already been reinvesting your **profits** from your investments/business or do you use your profits for other things? Please note, if you are using your profits for other reasons and you don't want to reinvest, that is perfectly fine. I am just showing you other ways and means of growing your investment portfolio.

Are you now going to start this process?   Yes/ No (Circle the appropriate one)

Why? Why not?

If you decide to invest as part of your game plan, then I would say it is up to you to decide what form of investment best suits you and what level of risk you are willing to take. The main point to bear in mind is that **you are prepared for the risk**. You should ideally have a healthy savings balance and be able to pay all your expenses comfortably at the end of each month.

Once this is the case, you will be prepared to invest, and the plan you have in place – as well as the peace of mind that comes with it – will help you to make wise decisions on your investment choices.

I would recommend researching the field/area you wish to invest in before investing your money. We do not want a situation where the money you sacrificed and saved for is then invested into a vehicle – be it financial or non-financial – that brings no profit or return or, even worse, the initial investment money is lost. We do not want this to happen. Therefore, it is important to study the investment vehicle carefully before investing.

I do believe that if you do not have an investment plan in place, you could end up gambling with your money by making unwise choices in your desperation to EARN some form of income or to generate money.

Makes some notes on what you are drawn to investing and explain why.

Different methods you can adopt when growing your investment fund

1) Putting money aside every month and growing this fund until you are ready to invest, e.g. in a business, property or even shares.

2) Drip-feeding money into an investment vehicle – be it a Stocks & Shares ISA (Individual Savings Account, available in England), or even into a private business where you invest money monthly.

Or

3) You can adopt the two approaches mentioned above and implement them at the same time if your INCOME AND EXPENDITURE STATEMENT has room for this. This means putting money aside into an INVESTMENT FUND and growing that money until you are ready and prepared to invest.

And

You can also drip-feed money into a private business or an ISA on a month-on-month basis.

Exercise T: Questions To Ask Yourself

Growing an investment fund.

How much money do you need to have saved in the **investment fund** before you can start investing?

Is it £1,000 or £5,000? More or less?

Do some homework into what you want to invest in and find out what sort of start-up capital is needed. Remember, an investment can also be starting a new business or going into partnership with someone. Jot down any notes here.

How many months or years do you need to save in the investment fund before you can start investing? Work out your calculations here.

Drip-feeding strategy

In some cases, you can start investing immediately – for instance, you can put your investment money into a stocks and shares ISA. Again, do your own homework and see what works best for you. How much can you invest?

If, at the moment, you do not know what to invest in but you feel certain an opportunity will arise someday, you want to be prepared with a readily available CASH FLOW for that time. Start your investment fund even if there is nothing to invest in now.

No matter what your age, bear in mind that it is never too early or too late to come into the investing arena. It all depends on the financial goals you set out for yourself, your time frames for achieving them, and your persistence towards gaining success in attaining them.

Having your family's support and agreement is vital on your journey to a successful financial game plan, especially in times of setback and discouragement.

Opportunities and risks

In the context of this workbook, OPPORTUNITIES are openings, occasions or chances to get involved with a great INVESTMENT: e.g. business, the stock market, property, etc. We mainly focus on having a lump sum investment fund (money) to invest in this next section and not so much on the drip-feeding approach where you put money monthly into shares or business, but both can still apply.

Opportunities can come in two forms:

Opportunities we find

The first are ones that we as individuals are on the lookout for. We train our eyes and ears to see and hear when they come our way. They could be a business venture, or the chance to buy a property at a fantastic bargain price, or you hear about an opportunity to invest in a good company or several companies on the stock exchange. Most of the time, these forms of opportunities present themselves to the individuals researching these areas and are not obvious to the general public.

Exercise U: Opportunities (1)

Are you on the lookout for opportunities?

Yes/No (Circle the appropriate answer).

Are you prepared for when those opportunities come?

Yes/No (Circle the appropriate answer)

Notes

_____

_____

_____

_____

_____

_____

_____

_____

_____

_____

Unexpected opportunities

The second form of opportunities comes along less often. However, when they do come they are a great chance to invest and grow money. Two examples that come to mind are 1) a stock-market crash (or what I term a 'stock-market sale') where you may have the opportunity to buy 'financially sound' shares of companies at a discounted price and 2) investing in a ground-breaking business or product that is about to be launched on the market.

These kinds of situations usually only happen once, twice or three times in a lifetime, and most of the time this type of information is in the public eye because it may affect society or some aspects of society. However, it is often only the ones who are prepared who are then able to take up this type of offer, even though everyone may know about it.

Exercise V: Opportunities (2)

Have you ever encountered such an opportunity? (And what was it?)

Were you prepared for the opportunity when it came?

How did it make you feel, being prepared for or missing out on the opportunity?

What sort of opportunity do you like or would like to get into?

As I have already said, **you must do your own homework beforehand** and ensure you get some expert advice before buying into any of these prospects.

I would like to reiterate here that the reason we are able to look for and take up such opportunity is because we are prepared. We have made our FINANCIAL PLAN, our CREDIT SCORE is good, we have manageable or no debt and, most importantly, we have savings for such a time as this. We are then able to easily take up such opportunities when they are presented to us.

Risks

> **RISK**
>
> The Oxford English Dictionary defines risk as 'the possibility of being exposed to danger or loss'.

Remember, INVESTMENT comes with a certain level of risk and you must be prepared to lose this money. No one wants to lose their hard-earned cash, but investments are not the same as savings, which offer safe returns.

An investment always comes with risk but, the risk **must** be calculated. A certain level of research must be put in first. Do not ever go into an opportunity blindly. You must thoroughly understand what you are putting your money into. This is about making your money work for you. The more prepared you are, the better your investment decisions will be.

However, there is a possibility we can lose our investment money, depending on the risk we take. That is why we separate out our savings from our investment fund. We know investments come with the risk of losing the investment money when taking up such opportunities.

By developing your thinking to look for opportunities, you will also increase your knowledge about them and thus maybe lessen the risk involved.

I recommend it is sometimes good to invest in things you are truly passionate or knowledgeable about. The more you know about a subject, the better the investment decision and the outcome, e.g. profitability.

Exercise W: Investing

What would you like to invest in (cars, the arts, property)?

Because of your knowledge and passion, you will be more likely to keep up-to-date with current information and trends, which will give you a greater insight into your investments. If you find your investment topic boring, you could find it arduous to oversee your investments and therefore less likely to pay as much attention to it – hence the risk!

It is good to visit a Financial Advisor for advice and knowledge and I recommend doing this. However, we must remember that we have our part to play also; it is our hard-earned money.

Therefore, the information in this chapter is to act as a guide only. It is up to you to do the relevant research and investments that best suit your needs and those of your family.

Notes

Fool-proof Your Action Plan

Jigsaw Completion

> *'Fool-proofing of a plan means making it so simple and easy to understand that it is unable to go wrong or be used wrongly'*
>
> —*Cambridge Dictionary*

In this chapter, we pull together your information – what you have learnt and found out, and your answers to the questions and exercises you have completed. The purpose of this is to now give a summary analysis, what I call 'the completion of the jigsaw'. You may have to go back and forth within the book for this assignment to find the answers from the previous exercises.

Summary analysis: Part 1

Firstly, decide which of the following four positions you are in, and put the relevant monthly profit or loss figure next to that description. You can get this information from the exercises in Chapters 1 and 2.

I am in the _____ position.

Debt

What is your average monthly loss?

_____

Those of you in a debt situation, I assume, would now want to make your way into the breakeven or savings position. If you have both savings and debt, the one with the greater amount will tell you which category you fall into. Please remember what we learnt in the debt chapter where we spoke about debt compounding: When debt burden becomes so large, it inevitably begins to progressively increase interest payments leading to greater debt, and this happens every month thereafter until the debt is paid off. This leads to a rapid expansion of interest payment on your debt.

Therefore, most of the time it is better to tackle the debt even when you have savings and put yourself in the debt category until it is cleared

Breakeven

What is your average monthly profit/loss? (For this position, it should ideally be roughly zero in a given month).

Those of you who find yourself here would ideally want to move to a SAVINGS or SAVINGS/INVESTMENT position.

Savings

What is your average monthly profit?

If you find yourself in this position, that is great news. However, you may want to define and allocate the purpose for your savings, or you may want to make your way into the savings & investments category. If you have both savings and debt, the one with the greater amount will tell you which category you fall into.

Savings and investments

What is your average monthly profit?

There may be those of you who may already find yourselves in this position but did not know how to solidify your finances and come up with a game plan.

Summary analysis: Part 2

We have now completed the information needed from Chapters 1 and 2. The next set of information will be taken from Chapter 3, *Finance Report Card*.

A credit report has become a fundamental piece of information in a person's financial outlook. It is a collection of information about the way an individual handles debt. This represents the creditworthiness of a person. Lenders use credit scores to determine who qualifies for a LOAN, at what INTEREST RATE and what CREDIT LIMITS

Exercise X: Your Credit Report

What does your credit report say?

Are you satisfied with the report or do you need to improve it? How can you do that?

Have you spoken to a credit reference agency to find out what methods you can introduce to improve your score? What are these methods?

How long will it take you to improve your score? Months or even years? Do you have a rough idea of the timescale? Contacting a credit reference agency will help give you an idea of time.

Summary analysis: Part 3

Now onto fool-proofing your Financial Game Plan.

What do I mean by 'fool-proofing'? In the previous chapters, I have recommended three funds that have very important purposes to any financial game plan. Actually, two are pivotal to your financial success.

1) **Miscellaneous fund** – for day-to-day miscellaneous, unbudgeted expenses that occur in our lives. This is the first of the pivotal funds.

2) **Savings fund** – for long-term savings, especially for the peace of mind and security it brings. This is the second of the pivotal funds.

3) **Investment fund** – for risk-taking/investment money to be used to grow wealth, but separate from the other funds so that you are able to bear the loss if anything goes wrong with your investments. This fund is fundamental for growing investments, but would not be considered a pivotal fund as not everyone wants to make or create an investment nest egg.

Miscellaneous fund

First things first: have you done the previous exercises and looked at your finances in order to allocate money for a miscellaneous fund? This fund is extremely important to have. Refer to Chapter 5, *Breakeven Analysis* for help to the answers for these two questions.

Yes/No (Circle the appropriate answer)

(A miscellaneous fund is pivotal to ensuring that you do not go into a debt situation or to avoid you tapping into your savings.)

What is the monthly amount to be introduced? _____

Savings fund

Exercise Y

Once you have your miscellaneous fund, are you able to find money from your monthly income and expenditure to allocate to savings?

Yes/No (Circle the appropriate answer)

If this is yes, what is the monthly amount you can save? _____

What are the purposes for your savings?

Remember, it is recommended by Financial Experts that you aim to save three to six months of monthly savings as a peace-of-mind fund in case of any emergency, e.g. redundancy, job loss, etc. This amount of money will help cover your bills as you rectify the problem.

If you did want to save three- to six-months' worth of expenses or even one-month expense cover, what amount would that be in total?

(An example of this would be if your **expenses** for the month is £985, then one-month's cover would be £985, three-months' cover would be £985 × 3 = £2,955 or six-months' expense cover would be £985 × 6 = £5,910.)

How long will it take you to save your target savings amount?

Example: If we take the three-month expense cover target of £985 per month × 3 months = £2,955. If we can save £100 per month, the length of time it would take us to save that would be:

£2,955 ÷ £100 per month = 29.5 (30) months.

What does that mean in years?

30 months ÷ 12 = 2 years, 6 months to reach our target.

Please do not let the length of time put you off. This is an excellent goal to work towards and the peace of mind that it brings you is worth its weight in gold…..a figure of speech, of course! Just think how grateful you would be that you had this fund if an unexpected event occurred that caused you to need it. I am sure you would sleep better at night just for knowing that.

Do you have any other savings goals in mind? Write them down in the notes section. Even if you can't start saving for them now, it is still good to write the target down as a reminder for the future. It could be to buy a car or save for a holiday, or even a wedding.

Investment fund

Exercise Z

Now we move on to the INVESTMENT FUND. After reading the previous chapters and doing the exercises, have you decided if you want to invest?

     Yes/No (Circle the appropriate answer)

If your answer is no, that is fine. A lot of people do not want or need the added stress that comes with investing. Investing can be very hard work at times with the added possibility of losing your hard-earned money. For those of you who want to invest, I hope I haven't put you off.

Do you know how much you would like to have saved before you start actually investing?

     Yes/No (Circle the appropriate answer)

If yes, how much can you realistically save? _____

It is fine if you do not know this answer. Continue to do your homework. The main thing though, is to be financially prepared for when such an opportunity arises. If you can, start the investment savings process now.

For what reason(s) will you be saving?

A word of caution: Do not be too anxious to jump into investing because you think you are missing out if you don't. **Patience** is one of the fundamental keys to investing, the second is **knowledge**: Learn, Learn, Learn!

Summary analysis: Part 4

Your income and expenditure

We now look at your current income and expenditure against your new adjusted income and expenditure, which will include a new section for savings and investments. You can get the answers for this spreadsheet from all the exercises previously done. We must remember that for our new adjusted Income and Expenditure spreadsheet, we will be **including the three funds**.

Not everyone will have all three funds, and that is fine for these purposes.

Chapter 1, *The Now* will give you the information for your current income and expenditure, which you will need to fill the information in the following Income and Expenditure spreadsheet.

You will then need to look at Chapters 2–7 to get the other information. For example, from Chapter 5, *Breakeven Analysis*, in the exercise **'Expense Reduction Analysis Spreadsheet'**, you would have looked at the areas you were able to reduce your costs and by how much. This is where you will now put that information, into this section.

This Income and Expenditure exercise may take some time to pull this information together, but please be patient and thorough otherwise you may miss a section.

Exercise A1: Income and Expenditure Spreadsheet Revised

Income

CATEGORY	*Current* MONTHLY AMOUNT	*New adjusted* Monthly Amount with *Funds*
INCOME:		
Wages/Salary after tax		
Government/State benefits		

(Continued on next page)

Income cont.

Any other income		
Total INCOME:		

Expenses

CATEGORY	*Current* MONTHLY AMOUNT	MONTHLY AMOUNT
EXPENSES:		
HOME:		
Mortgage or Rent		
Building Insurance		
Contents Insurance		
House Tax		
Council Tax		
Service Charges		
Other home charges		
Total HOME:		
TRANSPORTATION:		
Car Purchase payments		

(Continued on next page)

Insurance		
Tax		
Servicing /MOT		
Other transportation used (bus, tube, train, etc.)		
Total TRANSPORTATION:		
UTILITIES:		
Electricity		
Gas		
Water		
TV License		
Satellite/Cable		
Landline Telephone		
Mobile Telephone		
Broadband/ Wi-Fi		
Other Utilities		
Total UTILITIES:		

(Continued on next page)

FOOD		
Monthly grocery bill		
Lunches, snacks, etc.		
Meals out, takeaways		
Other food		
Total FOOD:		

ENTERTAINMENT:		
Memberships (gym, golf, etc.)		
Subscriptions (magazines, newspapers, films)		
Children's Activities (Scouts, ballet, drama, etc.)		
Other entertainment:		
Total ENTERTAINMENT		

DEBT PAYMENTS		
Credit cards		
Store cards		

(Continued on next page)

Bank loan		
Hire purchase		
Other loans		
Total DEBT REPAYMENTS:		

SAVINGS		
INVESTMENTS/SAVINGS:		
Savings (ISAs, Savings Accounts, etc.)		
Pensions		
Total INVESTMENTS/SAVINGS:		

OTHER UNSPECIFIED EXPENSES		
List anything not mentioned above, e.g. pet cost, etc.		
Total OTHER EXPENSES:		
Total SAVINGS, INVESTMENTS & EXPENSES		
PROFIT OR LOSS		

When completing your adjusted Income and Expenditure exercise, remember that hard credit enquiries can affect your credit score. Therefore, when looking to reduce costs, bear in mind that any changes to debt (for example credit card transfer, loans, insurances or mobile phone tariffs) can possibly affect your credit score. It is up to you to do the relevant research and adjustments that best suit you and your family needs.

Since each individual/family circumstance is different, the information this book provides acts as a guide only.

Our financial game plan is progressing. What we have done is to plan our finances in such a way that we can start getting our money working for us. Therefore, getting the Income and Expenditure spreadsheet correct is of paramount importance in the whole scheme of things. This will be the building block of our financial game plan.

Teatime

I want you to now sit back, take a few breaths and relax. Please remember, we do not want to rush this and get it wrong!

Then I want you to come back, sit and look at this spreadsheet again. Get really familiar with the information. Go back over your figures one by one, make sure they look right and have been correctly calculated. Get to know this spreadsheet and the information it contains. It is important to become comfortable with it.

A word of caution: New habits and costs

An important thing I must mention here is that, yes, we have written your new adjusted Income and Expenditure sheet. This is really great. The key here is to stick with it and REVIEW it on a regular basis.

I would recommend that you monitor this plan at least once a month. Ideally, it should be monitored two to three times a month, or even weekly.

> *You have just made adjustments to your habits and your spending and, it may surprise you, but if it is not reviewed regularly it can be very easy to slip back into old ways.*

In order for habits to take root, especially in this situation, your plan will need to be monitored and reviewed to see if you are coping well with it. Remember what I said before: it can take 21 days for a new habit to form.

It is good to state what times of the month (e.g. on the 1st of the month, at the end of the month, etc.) you will review and monitor your INCOME AND EXPENDITURE STATEMENT. You will need your most recent bank statement in order to do this effectively. Its purpose is really to see if you are staying within the expense budget you put in place, asking yourself tough questions along the way.

The following exercise will help you review your budget.

Exercise A2: Review

How often do you plan to review your income and expenditure spreadsheet?

_____

Is the budget working?   Yes/No (Circle the appropriate answer)

Why? Why not?

Did I set an unrealistic budget? (Make notes if necessary.)

Do I need to make some re-adjustments (i.e. major or minor corrections)?

What are these adjustments?

Monitor, Monitor, Monitor!!

I monitor my finances at least three to four times a MONTH

Notes

Your Future Financial Game Plan

The Roadmap

Now we will move onto writing up your future financial game plan in the context of all the exercises you have done so far.

> *It would be good to have a ten-year financial game plan.*
> *However, having a five-year plan is just as good.*

Nevertheless, for some this might be too far into the future so we will start with a one-year financial game plan, then move up to a five-year financial game plan. I have taken a copy of the one from my book *What's Your Financial Game Plan?* to help you see what it looks like and how simple it can be. As I said before: this workbook was never meant to be complicated.

This plan is not set in stone, it really is a framework for the direction you as individuals or families want to be heading in. When setting these financial goals, it is key that we make them SMART: **S**pecific, **M**easureable, **A**chievable, **R**ealistic and **T**ime-Based.

Example: A breakdown of a ten-year financial game plan:

Ten-year goal
- Generate the same amount or more money from my investments comparable to my paid salary. I can then resign from my job and work for myself.
- Have a healthy Savings Account with more than six-months' living expenses saved.
- Be able to enjoy the proceeds from my investments, e.g. holidays, a new car or even a house.
- Being able to give at least 5% or more of earnings to charities, good causes and loved ones when they are in need.

Strategy
- 10% of my salary goes to savings and another 10% of my salary goes towards investments

First three years
- Have as savings one- to three-months' living expenses (will keep this in a savings account).
- Have the equivalent of three months' salary saved as investments before investing.
- Live off the remaining 80% of salary.

Five years
- Continue saving 10% of salary.
- Have money invested in two ventures, with a return on these investments within three years.

(Continued on next page)

Ten-year goal completion
- Investments to generate good returns (income).
- Have a healthy savings balance in the bank account.
- Able to leave my job because my investment income can support my family and me.

The One-Year Plan

Let's now write up our one-year financial game plan. Again, you may need to refer to your answers to the previous exercises to be able to complete this as they will help you make a more informed future plan.

Bear in mind you do not need to answer all the questions suggested in the one-year, five-year or ten-year plans below. You only need answer what is relevant to you and your circumstances. Respond to the questions you have answers for. Make it as accurate as possible, with an element of flexibility. Remember this plan will be subject to changes from your personal life and from the world around you.

Each strategy for the plan has an example first before the question asking what your strategy is. Please don't think these examples are for YOUR game plan.

My One-Year Financial Plan

Strategy: e.g. 10% of my salary goes to savings and another 10% of my salary goes towards investments.

First year
- Have as savings, one- to three-months' living expenses (will keep this in a savings account).
- Have the equivalent of one month's salary saved in an investment fund.
- Live off the remaining 80% of salary.

What is your strategy?

My personal one-year financial game plan forecast

What financial category would I ideally get to? 1) debt 2) breakeven 3) savings 4) investing?

_____

What should my credit report and credit score improve by? (Please refer to Chapter 3, *Finance Report Card.*)

_____

(Remember, you can talk to the agencies to find out how you can improve your score if your score needs improving.)

* * * * *

Debts – refer to Chapter 4, *Debt Analysis*

I want to clear £...................... from my debts by the end of the year.

What would be the outstanding amount of my remaining debts? £......................

How much can I increase/decrease my **monthly** debt repayments by £......................

* * * * *

Savings – refer to Chapter 6, *Savings Analysis*

My savings account should have £...................... in it.

The purpose of my savings is: (e.g. peace of mind, buy a car, etc.)

I can increase/decrease my current monthly saving amount by £...........................

(Continued on next page)

Investments – refer to Chapter 7 *Savings and Investments Analysis*

My total investment fund should have £........................ saved to date.

I can increase/decrease my current **monthly** investment fund amount by £....................

Am I ready to invest?

      Yes/No (Circle the appropriate answer)

Do I have sufficient knowledge/information to invest?

      Yes/No (Circle the appropriate answer)

If no, what do I need to find out?

Would I like to invest in something?

      Yes/No (Circle the appropriate answer)

What is it likely to be? E.g. a property, business or even the stock market, etc.

This is, of course, after you have done your homework.

Congratulations! You have completed your one-year financial game plan forecast. I hope you enjoyed it and are ready to move onto the next section. I know some of you may not want to have a five-year or even a ten-year plan, but I am hoping that completing your one-year plan and realising how easy it was will stir you onto the next one.

I would recommend you try it, as to come back to a five-year plan in the future may mean re-familiarising yourself with this workbook all over again.

The Five-Year Plan

My Five-Year Financial Plan

Are there any adjustments to your strategy?

Strategy: e.g. 10% of my salary goes to savings and another 10% of my salary goes towards investments.

- Continue saving 10% of salary
- Have money invested in two ventures, with a return on these investments within three years.
- Live off the remaining 80% of salary.

What is your strategy?

What financial category would I ideally get to? 1) debt 2) breakeven 3) savings 4) investing?

I want to clear £........................ from my debts by the end of the five-year period or even be totally debt free.

My savings account should have £........................ in it.

Hopefully by the end of this period you would have been able to save at least three months' worth of peace-of-mind savings.

Other savings funds and their purpose:

I can increase/decrease my monthly saving amount by £........................

My investment fund should have £........................ saved to date. (Please use the space below for calculations.)

I can increase/decrease or even stop my monthly investment fund amount when I reach

£........................

Would I have started investing?

Yes/No (Circle the appropriate answer)

My return on investment (i.e. profit or loss) should roughly estimate £........................

Will I be reinvesting my profits for greater investment growth?

     Yes/No (Circle the appropriate answer)

What could I invest in?

The longer the planning period, the less precise/clear the answers are. Even businesses and corporations do these forecasts, and the further into the future they plan for, the less accurate the information becomes.

I need you to understand this in case you think it is an irrelevant exercise or are concerned that you couldn't provide a 'correct' answer. What this FORECAST does is give you a strategy to use as you progress with your finances. Remember, a forecast is always subject to changes and adjustments. Circumstances are constantly changing and so will these forecasts. For some of you, your strategy may change drastically while others may see your progression moving forward smoothly and in line with your forecast. I need you to bear this in mind

Now we tackle the big ten-year plan!!!

The Ten-Year Plan

My Ten-Year Financial Plan

Are there any adjustments to your strategy? For example, I could continue to save but I am now only saving 5% of my salary because my savings balance is healthy. I do not need to put money into the investment fund because my returns on investments are good.

Commitment and sacrifice have paid off.

Achievements in ten years' time

- Have cleared all my debts.
- I maintained a good credit score.
- Have a healthy savings balance in the bank account.
- Able to leave my job because my investments are generating sufficient or more than sufficient income.
- Have paid off my mortgage.

What are your goals/dreams?

What financial category would I ideally get to? 1) debt 2) breakeven 3) savings 4) investing?

Cleared all my debt (except maybe for my mortgage): £......................... in debts at the end of the ten-year period or even be totally debt free.

My savings account should have £.........................Hopefully by then you would have been able to save at least three-months', but more like six-months' worth of peace-of-mind savings.

Other savings funds and their purpose:

I can increase/decrease my monthly saving amount when I reach £........................

My investment fund should have £........................ saved to date.

I can increase/decrease or even stop my monthly investment fund amount when I reach

£........................

Are investments bringing in a good return?

    Yes/No (Circle the appropriate answer)

My return on investment (i.e. profit or loss) should roughly estimate £........................

Will I reinvest my profits for greater investment return?

    Yes/No (Circle the appropriate answer)

If I want to, am I generating enough income from investments so that I can go part-time or even resign from my job and work full-time in the business/investment?

    Yes/No (Circle the appropriate answer)

Finally, we have completed the ten-year forecast. This is a big achievement. Most individuals/families do not do this type of exercise.

What this forecast does is give you some goals to work towards. It also helps clarify the journey.

Finally, this forecast makes the goals/targets achievable and realistic based on all the previous exercises you would have done from this book.

That is why we use calculations. These exercises are based on realistic numbers and are not guesses.

The journey

Well, it has been a journey and a half. There is only one more exercise that you now really need to do before you can take a rest from this book. I am sure you are looking forward to a rest as the exercises have been quite intense, and some of them would have had you thinking really deeply.

Getting this far and doing the majority of the exercises was no easy feat. I personally know that what I have asked of you in this workbook was intense and required a lot of your time, effort and concentration. Hopefully this will benefit you both now and in the future.

Unfortunately, by writing up your financial game plan and knowing the state of your finances now does not mean a successful future. This was just the starting point. As time continues you will need to monitor:

Monitor, Monitor, Re-adjust – and then Monitor some more.

It will take discipline, dedication and commitment. I know this from personal experience. However, the gain often far outweighs the pain. They are your finances, and now the changes can begin.

Let's recap on what we have accomplished:

- ❖ Defined which financial categories we are currently in.

- ❖ Ascertained which financial category we would like to attain in the future.

- ❖ Discovered the importance of having a good credit score.

- ❖ Written up a new Income and Expenditure Statement, which should definitely include a miscellaneous fund, and ideally should also include a savings fund – and for those who want to invest, an investment fund.

- ❖ Written our one-year financial goals/strategy or targets.

- ❖ Looked at our five-year financial plan and where we would ideally want to be.

- ❖ Finally, we looked at a ten-year plan.

Your achievements in completing this book are many:

1. You have a plan.

2. It is a sensible strategy.

3. It fits in with the lifestyle you want without getting into senseless debt.

4. You are able to stick with the plan. This is very important. There is no sense in creating a strategy you cannot stick with. Set a realistic plan.

Then there is the bonus of peace of mind. This is fundamental to the whole process.

Notes

Conclusion

Where do we go from here?

Finally, we have reached the last chapter. I am sure you must be relieved and glad. It has been an intense journey. I am also sure that after all these exercises and calculations you may now have a clearer view of what guidelines you would like to implement. We covered guidelines in the first section of this book. Here we revisit this topic now that you are armed with your new plan.

A guideline is a statement of principles put forward to set standards or determine a course of action.

It is a set of principles that govern the course of action you want to take with your finances. It is recognising what you hold as important or that you do not want to compromise on.

For the sake of finalisation and completeness, here is the final exercise. Take a moment to revisit the guidelines that you wrote down at the start and see what has changed. Write down your revised set of guidelines here so that you don't forget them.

My Guidelines

Previously, a few of you may have thought the investment section unattainable, possibly due to *your age* or *your current financial position*.

Please do not let these factors dictate to you where you will be in five or ten years' time. You should set your own financial future and try not to let society or circumstances set it for you, even though they might try to.

Another point I would like to stress is that this is a first-level start to a financial game plan, what I would call the beginners guide. Financial game plans can be extremely complex with lots of other complicated spreadsheets and scenarios – for example, tax issues, adjustments for inflation, etc. Therefore, for some of you, you would have been far ahead of this plan. That is great news. However, for others this has been a major practical start in getting your finances under control and making sure it is heading in the right direction.

> *If you want to go further with your money game plan and need help, please join me on my website, www.whatsyourfinancialgameplan.com, where we delve even further into personal finances.*

There are plenty of places online where you can do some research yourself. Again, I say to you WELL DONE! What you have achieved in completing this book is excellent and you should feel really proud of yourself.

The important thing to take away is that it doesn't stop here. After reaching so far on this journey, I hope that you continue with the same zeal and passion in achieving your financial game plan as you have shown when writing it.

I would now recommend that you cut out or photocopy the major pages of this book that are relevant to you and stick it where you can see or review it regularly. I would also recommend having a personal finance file and putting these important pages in there so you can review them regularly, along with bank statements, regular bills etc. so that you can monitor your finances.

Some advice here: it is important that you monitor your finances regularly – at least once a month. Additionally, make sure that you do an annual review of your financial game plan. See if you are on track or need to re-adjust it. I must stress this is extremely important.

A major milestone in your financial roadmap has now been completed. It is now up to you though to make sure you monitor and attain those goals.

Remember we live in a dynamic, constantly changing economy. Your financial game plan is not necessarily set in stone. There will be times of adjustments or occurrences that can propel you forward even faster than you expected or set you back more than you anticipated. Be aware these situations do occur. Sometimes they are great when they happen and you jump for joy, but there are other times they can leave you feeling very despondent. But know that this does not mean you have failed in your game plan, it just means you have had a setback. Unfortunately, setbacks are part of life. The key is you now have knowledge on how to create a solid financial game plan. No one can take that away from you. So if the bad times come, re-adjust your finances and get back in the race.

I am of the opinion that if we have knowledge then we should learn from it and apply it to our lives. I do hope this is what you will do. I trust the majority of you reading this workbook will thrive with this new ammunition you have for making a success of your personal finances.

As I previously mentioned in the introduction of this book, bear in mind as you go through the exercises in this workbook that each individual/family circumstance is different. Therefore, it is up to you to do the relevant research and adjustments that best suit you and your family needs. Further information of organisations to help you can be found in the Useful Information section at the end of the book.

The information this book provides is to act as a guide only.

Closing thought

A final thought before I close off this book and something that I said in my previous book.

There are times when circumstances occur that are way beyond our control, and no MISCELLANEOUS FUND or SAVINGS FUND can stop us getting into a debt situation. It could be because of medical reasons, redundancy, a death in the family, or any other situation that can lead to us having no choice but to take on an amount of debt with the hope that fortunes will change in the future. This can happen to anyone, even to those who are excellent with finances. These are sometimes unfortunate circumstances, but again are usually extreme cases and I want to say for those individuals who find themselves in this position that I sympathise and I understand that these situations do occur. Regardless of this, I do believe you must continue to be wise with your finances, even if it seems beyond your control and even hopeless.

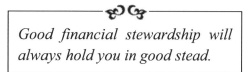

Good financial stewardship will always hold you in good stead.

Though it may mean nothing to you right now reading this book, there is always HOPE.

✳ ✳ ✳ ✳

If you enjoyed this book and found it useful, would you mind taking a few minutes to write a review and post it on Amazon.co.uk or whatsyourfinancialgameplan.com? Your comments help others know what to expect when reading this book and applying the exercises. I look forward to reading your comments.

Notes

How can you be more successful with your money?

**Continue developing your own financial game plan with
Neala Okuromade**

Now that you have worked through the workbook you can continue your money journey by visiting the website

www.whatsyourfinancialgameplan.com

Take advantage of a free eBook, videos and blogs that teach valuable methods and techniques to make sure you get the greatest potential from your money.

Neala encourages you; individuals, students, families and even small businesses to explore and enhance your money skills and knowledge. She examines different money topics, outlining principles and practical guidelines for successful money management.

No matter who you are, if you learn and apply these suggestions and tips, your financial capacity will increase and your efforts will be multiplied.

Brad & Adam Series, The Book:
WHAT'S YOUR FINANCIAL GAME PLAN?

By Neala Okuromade

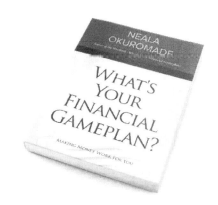

What does your financial situation look like?

What's Your Financial Game Plan? –The book takes readers on a step-by-step journey to learn the principles needed to develop a fool-proof financial strategy for their situation, whatever that might be. It opens their eyes to the possibilities that money has to offer if they utilise it wisely and also show them what happens when they don't.

Through the stories of four friends who have the same job with the same salary, we see how they end up in totally different financial positions. What happened? One used his money to his advantage and ended up financially successful, another was able to pay off her mortgage much earlier than expected, while the others ended up in debt – and very stressed and depressed.

Filled with in-depth insights and practical advice, *What's Your Financial Gameplan?* will show you how to incorporate certain proven strategies to change the way you see and handle your finances. You'll discover :

- ✓ Financial planning
- ✓ The power of compounding, positive and negative
- ✓ The importance of a credit report
- ✓ Debt: good and bad
- ✓ A savings strategy
- ✓ An investment-making approach

This book will hopefully inspire and lead you to financial success, whatever that might look like for you personally.

Glossary

Annual Percentage Rate (APR)   it is basically how much a person's borrowing will cost over the period of an average year, over the term of your debt.

Asset   Any item of 'economic value' owned by an individual, company or government; especially that which could be converted to cash. Examples are cash, property, car, and stocks and shares.

Bank Loan   *see* LOANS

Bankruptcy   The legal process whereby a person declares their inability to pay their DEBTS. Upon a court declaration, a person surrenders their ASSETS (i.e. house, car, etc.) and is relieved from the payment of previous debts. In the U.S. and U.K., this status is established through legal procedures involving a petition by the bankrupt person or entity, or by its creditors.

Blacklisted   A person under suspicion, considered untrustworthy, disloyal, to be boycotted or penalised, especially by a government or an organisation. In the context of this book, it is the person's inability or unwillingness to pay their obligations that leads to their name being blacklisted.

Bonus   Something given or paid in addition to what is usual or expected. It is often a sum of money or an equivalent given to an employee on top of the employee's usual salary or compensation.

Breakeven   In general, the point at which gains equal losses. For this book, breakeven is when monthly INCOME equals monthly EXPENSES.

Budget   An estimation of our INCOME and EXPENSES over a specified future period of time. A budget can be made for a person, family, business, government or country. Budgets are usually compiled and re-evaluated periodically and adjustments are made to budgets based on the goals of the budgeting person, country or organisation.

Cash Flow   *see* SAVINGS

Compounding   *see* Debt Compounding and Wealth Compounding

Court Judgment   *see* Financial Court Judgment

Credit   An arrangement between a financial institution, usually a bank, and a customer that establishes a maximum LOAN balance that the bank will permit the borrower to maintain. The borrower can draw down on the line of credit at any time, as long as he or she does not exceed the maximum set in the agreement.

Credit Cards   A small plastic card issued to individuals as a system of payment. It allows people who have a card to buy goods and services now, and requires that person to pay for these goods and services in the future, usually with interest (*see* INTEREST RATES). Some stores issue cards for purchase of their goods and services. These are known as Store Cards.

Credit History or **Credit Report**   A record of an individual's past borrowing and repayments, including information about late payments and BANKRUPTCY.

Credit Limit   The maximum amount of CREDIT that a bank or other lender will extend to a customer, or the maximum that a CREDIT CARD company will allow a card holder to borrow on a single card.

Credit Score (or Credit Rating)   A credit score represents the creditworthiness of that person. Lenders use credit scores to determine who qualifies for a LOAN, at what INTEREST RATE, and what CREDIT LIMITS.

A County Court Judgment (CCJ)   is a type of court order in England, Wales and Northern Ireland that might be registered against you if you fail to repay money you owe.

Debt   An obligation or liability to pay or render something, usually money, to someone else. If an individual spends more than they earn, then after a while they will accumulate debt and this always needs to be repaid. They may need to pay back a bank, building society, family or friend, but the money will need to be paid back depending on the terms and conditions negotiated.

Debt Compounding   When debt burden becomes so large it inevitably begins to progressively increase interest payments leading to greater debt. (Interest upon interest.)

Deficit   In economics, a deficit is a shortfall in revenue, a DEBT. In more specific cases it may refer to, for example, a trade deficit, when the value of imports exceeds the value of exports in a country.

Deposit   A sum payable as a first instalment on the purchase of something or as a pledge for a contract, the balance being payable later: The one we are familiar with is a deposit paid for a house.

Disbursement   The act of paying out or disbursing money. Disbursements can include money paid out to run a business, spending cash and grant payments.

Earnings[1]   (in relation to employment) any salary, wage or fee or any other profit or incidental benefit of any kind obtained by an employee in return for services given.

Earnings[2]   The amount of profit that a company produces during a specific period, which is usually defined as a quarter or a year. Earnings typically refer to after-TAX net income.

Entertainment   All the costs associated within the spreadsheets listed in this book; e.g. dining out, going to the cinema or theme park and any other cost that may fall into this category that is specific to you.

Envelope System   Where an individual puts a set amount of money aside on a month-by-month basis for certain categories such as food, shopping, eating out and other miscellaneous items.

Expense (expenditure)   An outflow of money to another person or group to pay for an item or service, or for a category of costs. Buying food, clothing, furniture or a car is often referred to as an expense. An expense is a cost that is 'paid', usually in exchange for something of value.

Exponentially   describes a rate of increase that is extremely quick, appearing to grow rapidly.

Finance Counsellor   A person whose job is to give financial advice and help to people so they can manage their income and expenses, including debt, more successfully.

Financial Advisor   A professional who provides financial advice or guidance to customers for compensation. Financial advisors can provide many different services, such as investment management, income tax preparation and estate planning.

Forecast   Estimates a person's future financial outcomes by examining their historical financial data i.e. anticipate end results/goals based on previous information. Companies use financial forecasting to determine how they should allocate their budgets for a future period

Financial Investment Vehicles   Financial instruments whose value is determined directly by the financial markets. These vehicles can include investing in the stock market e.g. via shares, bonds, ETFs (exchange traded funds) or unit trusts.

Financial Plan   A series of steps or goals used by an individual to accomplish a final financial goal or set of goals, e.g. elimination of DEBT, early repayment of a MORTGAGE, etc.

Fixed Rule Approach   In the context of this book the 'fixed rule approach' is when you apply a fixed monetary amount as an expense to your monthly income, e.g. saving £50 every month.

Guidelines   A statement of principles put forward to set standards or determine a course of action. In this book, it is a set of principles that govern the course of action you want to take with your finances.

Grants   These are non-repayable funds given by one party, often a government department, corporation, foundation or trust, to a recipient, e.g. an educational institution, charity, business or an individual.

Hard Credit Enquiries   usually occur when a financial institution, such as a lender or credit card issuer, checks your credit report when making a lending decision.

Hidden Trap   One-off expenses that haven't been budgeted for or thought about, such as a fridge needing to be fixed or the purchase of a birthday present. The person is under the illusion that their total monthly bills are covered. These situations not planned for then leads the individual into unnecessary DEBT.

High-Risk Investment   INVESTMENTS that involve a greater than usual amount of risk when investing. A fundamental idea in finance is the relationship between RISK and return. The greater the amount of risk that an investor is willing to take on, the greater the potential return. The reasoning for this is that investors need to be compensated for taking on additional risk. *see also* INVESTMENT.

Hire Purchase A method of buying goods through making instalment payments over time. Under a hire purchase contract, the buyer leases the goods and does not obtain ownership until the full amount of the contract is paid.

Income The flow of cash or cash equivalents received from work (wage or salary), capital (interest or profit), or land (rent).

Income and Expenditure Statement A statement to measure an individual's financial performance over a specific period of time. A person's financial performance is assessed by giving a summary of how that person incurs their income and expenses. It also shows the profit or loss incurred over a specific period, typically a month, quarter or year

INTEREST *SEE* INTEREST RATES

Interest-Only Mortgage A type of MORTGAGE where a person is only required to pay off the INTEREST that arises from the mortgage money borrowed, leaving the capital still owing.

Interest Rates The rate charged or paid for using money. You are charged an interest rate (payment on top of the amount) when you borrow money and paid an interest rate when you loan money (an amount on top of the loan amount). Placing money in a SAVINGS FUND or INVESTMENT FUND is like a loan to the bank, so you are paid interest on your savings. With CREDIT CARDS, LOANS and MORTGAGES the interest rate directly influences the cost of borrowing. Lower interest rates mean you'll pay a lower cost (for example 5% of your DEBT), while higher interest rates mean a higher cost (for example 18% of your debt).

Investment Putting money into FINANCIAL or NON-FINANCIAL VEHICLE or instrument that has some degree of RISK, in the hope of seeing the money grow significantly over time. *see also* HIGH-RISK INVESTMENT and LOW-RISK INVESTMENT.

Investment Fund For the context of this book, it is a fund used solely and specifically for investing. An individual puts money aside from their salary into this fund until they are ready to invest.

Investment Vehicle Any method that individuals or businesses can invest in and, ideally, grow their money. There is a wide variety of investment vehicles and many investors choose to hold at least several types in their portfolios. *see also* FINANCIAL INVESTMENT VEHICLE and NON-FINANCIAL INVESTMENT VEHICLE.

Liability An obligation that legally binds an individual, company or government to settle a DEBT. When one is liable for a debt, they are responsible for paying the debt.

Loans The temporary provision of money (usually at interest); a bank loan – a loan made by a bank; to be repaid with interest on or before a fixed date.

Loans and Credit Cards Repayments   A heading in the spreadsheets of this book that represents the monthly payments an individual pays towards clearing his debt balance. DEBT balance is made up of all loans excluding MORTGAGES, all CREDIT CARDS and STORE CARDS and any PAYDAY LOANS one may have.

Low-Risk Investment   INVESTMENTS that are likely to be successful, or unlikely to be connected with danger or problems. Returns are unlikely to deviate from expectations. The main reason individuals buy low-risk investments is because there is only a very small chance that they will lose capital. *see also* INVESTMENT.

Mortgages   A LOAN secured against a property (usually a house) to be repaid within or by a set period of time, normally twenty to thirty years. *see also* RE-MORTGAGE

Non-Financial Investment Vehicle   INVESTMENTS that do not deal with financial or investment-related goods or services that individuals or businesses can invest in and, ideally, grow their money. These can include running your own small business, INVESTING in an already existing business or investing in property, either commercial or residential.

One-Off Expenses   Costs that occur in our day-to-day lives. It covers EXPENSES of items that would eventually need to be replaced or fixed for example kettle, iron and blender. It includes gifts for birthdays, weddings, anniversaries, also small emergency bills and many other situations that crop up day-to-day.

One-Off Expense Fund   Otherwise known as a Rainy-Day Fund. This can be defined as a fund for small, miscellaneous costs that arise in our day-to-day lives.

Opportunities   In the context of this book, opportunities are openings, occasions or chances to get involved with a great INVESTMENT. They can be business, stock market or property.

Overdraft Facility   When money is withdrawn from a bank account and the available balance goes below zero. In this situation, the account is said to be 'overdrawn'. An overdraft facility is a prior agreement with the bank or account provider for an agreed amount to be withdrawn below the zero balance.

Payday Loans   A payday loan is a small, short-term, unsecured LOAN 'regardless of whether repayment of loan is linked to a borrower's payday'. Payday advance loans rely on the consumer having previous payroll and employment records. Legislation regarding payday loans varies widely between different countries.

Pension   A regular payment made during a person's retirement from an investment fund that a person or their employer has contributed to during their working life.

Percentage Rule Approach   In the context of this book the 'percentage rule approach' is applying a percentage (%) of your monthly INCOME to an expense such as the example used in the savings chapter with Saving 10% of a monthly income. *see also* FIXED RULE APPROACH

Quarterly Income   Costs occurring or appearing at three month intervals e.g. telephone bills or car road tax.

Rainy-Day Fund   *see also* ONE-OFF EXPENSE FUND

Re-mortgage   Paying off an existing MORTGAGE and entering into a new one, usually to obtain a lower rate of interest or a larger loan. This is the process where a mortgage on a property is moved from one lender to another. The new mortgage is used to repay the existing lender and at the same time additional funds may be raised for other purposes.

Risk   The possibility of being exposed to danger or loss. Financially it is the probability that an actual return on an investment will be lower than the expected return.

Savings   Putting money into virtually RISK-free FINANCIAL VEHICLES or instruments where it can grow slowly and safely over time. It is important to understand that saving is not risk-taking and brings in little or no return. This money should be put into an INTEREST-bearing account or into a unit trust cash fund. This money is not for investing but for safe return over time.

Saving Fund   Generally a fund available for long-term or short-term goals. It can also exist simply for 'peace of mind'.

Soft Credit Enquiries   Usually occur when a person or company checks your credit report as part of a background check. Examples can include employer background checks, getting pre-approved for credit card offers, and checking your own credit score.

Store Cards   *see* CREDIT CARDS

Surplus   A situation in which INCOME exceeds EXPENDITURE, exports exceed imports, or profits exceed losses. A surplus is the opposite of a DEFICIT. When a country exports more than it imports, it is said to have a trade surplus.

Taxes   A means by which governments finance their EXPENDITURE by collecting a contribution from citizens and corporate entities.

Transportation Costs   These are all the costs necessary for running and maintaining a car. These costs cover car payment, insurance, TAXES, fuel and maintenance costs. This section also includes all other costs associated with you and your family's travel i.e. using the buses, trains etc.

Utilities   In the context of this book 'utilities' mentioned in the spreadsheets listed is an everyday necessity cost to the home. Utilities cover water bills, electricity and gas bills, telephone services and other essentials.

Wealth   Wealth is defined in this book as 'Possessing well-being, happy, comfortable or having an abundance of valuable possessions or money'. It can be a measure of the value of all of the assets of worth owned by a person, community, company or country.

Wealth Compounding   The ability of an asset to generate EARNINGS, which are then reinvested in order to generate their own earnings. In other words, compounding refers to generating earnings from previous earnings such as interest on interest.

Useful Information

For more information on Your Financial Game plan

Website

www.whatsyourfinancialgameplan.com

Email

neala@whatsyourfinancialgameplan.com

Advice Centres

Citizens Advice Bureau

www.citizensadvice.org.uk

The Citizens Advice Bureau helps many people in Britain to resolve their money issues by providing free, independent and confidential advice every year. You can obtain help via the phone, by email or by visiting one of their local branches near you.

National Debtline

www.nationaldebtline.co.uk

Phone: 0808 808 4000

Consumer Credit Counselling Service (CCCS), now called Stepchange Debt Charity

www.stepchange.org

Phone: 0800 138 1111

Wade House

Merrion Centre

Leeds LS2 8NG

CAP (Christians Against Poverty)

www.capuk.org

Jubilee Mill,

North Street, Bradford

BD1 4EW

Credit Report and Advice Centres

Experian

www.experian.co.uk

Phone: 0344 481 0800 or 0800 013 88 88

Credit Expert

PO Box 7710
Nottingham
NG80 7WE

Noddle (Free credit report and credit score)
www.noddle.co.uk

Equifax
www.equifax.co.uk
Customer Service Centre
PO Box 10036
Leicester
LE3 4FS

Check My File
www.checkmyfile.com
Phone: 0800 612 0421
Chynoweth House
Trevissome Park
Blackwater
Truro
TR4 8